GIS Guidebook:

WRITING ARCADE EXPRESSIONS

for ArcGIS Pro

By David W. Allen, GISP

GIS Guidebooks Press

Published

Gis Guidebook: Writing Arcade Expressions for ArcGIS Pro

US Government Restricted / Limited Rights: Any software

ArcGIS, ArcGIS Online, and ArcGIS Pro is a registered trademark of Esri, Inc. Efforts have been made to respect trademarked information with the use of capitals and specific mentions of trademarks where appropriate.

Published by GIS Guidebooks Press

Www.GISGuidebooks.com

Corsicana, TX

info@GISGuidebooks.com

ISBN-13: 978-0-578-53300-1

About the Author

David Allen has been working with GIS since 1983, developed the GIS system for the City of Euless and has worked there over 30 years, taught evening classes in the GIS program at Tarrant County College for over 18 years, and has published six other bestselling books on GIS. He knows this stuff inside and out ... and he has a great knack at being able to explain complex topics in a simple way. He has been working with ArcGIS Pro since the first Beta, has traveled to Redlands many times to work with the developers and test these new tools, and is continually working on new methods and ideas of how this stuff can best be put to best use.

Gis Guidebook: Writing Arcade Expressions for ArcGIS Pro

Table of Contents

Chapter 6 – Working With Dates

Setting up and formatting dates in your expressions

- *Exercise 9 – Writing date expressions*

Using the Date() functions

Chapter 7 – Writing Geometry Functions

Arcade has specific code to handle geometry features directly

- *Exercise 10 – Working with the Area() function*

Writing geometry analysis expressions in ArcGIS Online

- *Exercise 11 – Overlay analysis in AGOL*

Checking topology conditions with Arcade

- *Exercise 12 – Geometry layer overlap condition*

Building Array() and Dictionary() items

Working in the Arcade Playground

- *Exercise 13 – Testing code in the playground*

Putting a dictionary to use

Rafael's Challenge (Five Challenges)

Author's Introduction

I hope you are as excited about Arcade as I was when I first heard about it. There has always been a problem with using other people's data and not being able to access field values or do calculations that they didn't provide. But now Arcade solves all that. Plus it's a great way to format your labels and provide very interesting and engaging information in your pop-up windows. Arcade expressions can be as simple or complex as you like, allowing you to work within a single layer, or do cross layer analysis.

This book will start with very basic ideas of what Arcade is and how it works as a programming language. Many of the layout rules and code construction techniques are shown. But be aware that a book can't be a do-all end-all explanatory text and show every possible application of Arcade using your specific data. So the exercises contained will show many of the functions used in a variety of ways, then with this understanding of how things work you will be able to design and write new Arcade expressions that can achieve totally new things using data that is accessible to you.

Also, the data used here is totally and completely irrelevant. Please don't get hung up on the idea that some polygons represent a certain type of data or that some points represent data that you have no interest in. They are all points, lines, and polygons. If you don't like the idea of working with lemonade stand locations in census tracts, pretend that they are temperature sensing stations in lava fields. It doesn't matter, they're still just points and polygons. When you complete an exercise you might want to find some of your own data that is similar and try to replicate the lesson. It would be good practice! You might even try a different approach or even different tools. You know what they say about programming: It doesn't matter if the journey is short or long; people marvel at the result.

Some of the exercises will use ArcGIS Pro and include projects and data, some will use ArcGIS Online and pull in Esri Living Atlas data, and some are a combination of both. It's important in these exercises to use data that you can't edit or alter because that's where Arcade really shines.

It is expected that you already know how to use ArcGIS Pro and ArcGIS Online before starting this book. No instruction will be given on how to open project documents, how to access menu tools, how to navigate through AGOL, etc … If you are not comfortable working in ArcGIS Pro and ArcGIS Online then I would suggest starting with a book on that topic.

Throughout the book you will also see "Rafael's Question", which is a question students typically ask in the classroom except in this situation I have to both ask and answer them. You will also find "Rafael's Challenge" at the end of the book where you will take techniques you've learned and apply them to a new Arcade expression with minimal instruction. Helpful tips are given that you can reference as you solve the dilemma.

Dig in, have fun, and learn to program in Arcade!

DWA

The exercise data and materials can be found and downloaded at

https://GISGuidebooks.com/Arcade

Chapter 1—The Basics of Arcade Expressions

How does Arcade code differ from other languages?

Arcade is a new expression writing language invented for the ArcGIS platform that will work without modification across many aspects of the software. This portability means that expressions you write can be read and executed on the desktop, online, or in a mobile application. The functions are easy to understand and you will find that they mimic many existing programming languages with many of the same constructs and general structure. The large difference, however, is that Arcade includes expressions that are specific to working with spatial data in the ArcGIS environment and can be used in ways that other programming languages would have a struggle. The other major difference between Arcade and a programming language is that Arcade can not be used to author stand-alone scripts or programs – it is used only within the confines of ArcGIS software.

Every programming language has a basic set of rules for how the actual code is written and formatted, and Arcade scripts are no different. The list below shows some of the basic structural rules, and other will be discussed later:

Case insensitive – variables and function names can use upper or lower case interchangeably

Comments – any line preceded by two forward slashes is a comment and will not be executed. Multiple line comments can be bracketed with a forward slash and asterisk, then closed with an asterisk and forward slash.   /* … comments here … */

Multi-line statements – Arcade will read across multiple lines. If a statement still needs more parameters at the end of a line, the next line will automatically be read as a part of the same function. If a statement is complete at the end of a line, the next line will automatically be read as a new statement. Statements can be separated by semi-colons, but doing so isn't required.

Variables – variables are declared with the var function and a single equals sign (var =) and their data type is automatically detected by the format used in the declaration. After they are declared they can be redefined (or recast) with a simple equation.

Return – the last line in an Arcade expression will automatically be seen as the value which will be returned to the calling program. The line may include the function 'return' but in most cases it isn't necessary. The most prominent use of Return will be when using logic statements and jumping out of the middle of a script.

Operators – Arcade respects the usual mathematical operators like Greater Than (>), Less Than (<), Greater than or equal to (>=), and Less Than or Equal To (<=). Normal math operators are also used like add (+), subtract (-), multiple (*), and divide (/) as well as the high level math operators like sine, cosine, tangent, and others.

This set of code demonstrates some of these basic structural components:

```
// This is a comment

Var LandValue = 80000  // Note the use of upper and lower case in the variable name

var housevalue = 193500 // All lower case variable name … doesn't matter

/* The next statement will return the total assessed value

back to the labeling process that called it.

Note this use of a multi-line comment

and that the case in the variables is different

than the declaration statement */

landvalue + HouseValue
```

Every language has its own unique ways of handling code, and it's just a matter of remembering what this one uses so that you don't wind up spending hours troubleshooting code only to find a misplaced comma or decimal point.

Arcade Profiles

The areas in which Arcade can be used are known as an *execution profile*. These profiles include a text based alias, attribute rules, field calculations, labels, values for a pop-up or identify window, and more which will be discussed later. Any of these can be derived from the spatial data in your project, and certain global variables allow you direct access to this data. The **$feature** variable references a one-by-one iteration through the current layer being worked with, the **$layer** variable references all the features in a layer, the **$map** variable references the set of layers within the current map, and the **$datastore** variable references a feature set collection that can be created using other functions. These global variables are accessed different in each of the profiles, so more about this will be explained in the exercises.

As an example, if the set of code above was drawing the values of the land and house from the attributes in a feature layer it might look like this:

```
//The layer has a field called HouseVal and a field called LandVal

//In this example, the attributes names are all cap for emphasis

var LandValue = $feature.HOUSEVAL

var housevalue = $feature.LANDVAL

/* The last statement will return the total assessed value

back to the labeling process that called it – without using the RETURN function */

landvalue + HouseValue
```

This expression basically says "store the feature attribute value from the field HOUSEVAL into a variable called LandValue, then store the feature attribute value from the field LANDVAL into a variable called house-value, then add the two together and send the result back to the labeling engine'.

Rafael's Question: Was it necessary to use variables and then add the variable together to get the answer? Could you just add the two attributes together and return that?

Yes, that same code could be much simpler:

```
//Return total assessed value

$feature.HOUSEVAL + $feature.LANDVAL
```

All of that was boiled down to one line of code but it was important to see it with the variable declarations in order to understand what it is truly accomplishing.

Note: It is assumed that you are familiar with ArcGIS Pro and can navigate through the menus, use different panes, open attribute tables, change parameters, and generally work through the functions of ArcGIS Pro and ArcGIS Online. If not, please start with a book on the basics of ArcGIS Pro / ArcGIS Online and come back to Arcade when you are more comfortable with the software. No addition instruction will be given on how to access these basic features of the software.

Before you begin the exercises, please retrieve the support materials from this location:

https://GISGuidebooks.com/Arcade

Creating your first Arcade Expression

That code seems simple when you look at it, but there are still parts of this that are unique to Arcade that are better explained in their use. You will make the label expression described above in an ArcGIS Pro project and see it in action.

Exercise 1 – Using attributes in a label expression

You will start in the simplest of the various profiles—the label attribute profile.

1 **Start ArcGIS Pro and open Exercise 1 from the supplied materials and zoom to the Area 1 bookmark, if necessary.**

You will see that labeling is turned on for this layer and is showing the subdivision name. The goal is to change this to the total property value – even though there isn't a field in the data for total property value.

2 **Highlight the Property Tax Value layer in the Contents pane.**

3 **Select Labeling from the Feature Layer area of the ribbon menu.**

The labeling engine is one of the profiles in which you can write Arcade expressions, and certain of the global variables will be available here. The most prominent will be $feature, which because you have highlighted a layer in the Contents pane will reference the PropertyTaxValue layer. All the attributes in this layer can be accessed by adding $feature to the front of them. But relax, this is done automatically!

4 **In the upper left, find the Field entry box and click the Expression** ⌂ **icon next to it .**

Note that the default language is Arcade. In the labeling box you see the existing label expression, which you will replace with the new calculated expression.

5 **Delete the expression $feature.Prop_Des_1.**

6 **In the fields list, find the field House Value and double click it. It is added to the expression.**

7 **Next type a plus sign, then find the field Land Value and add it to the expression. When finished, click Validate** ✓ **then Apply.**

That expression is the same as the example above, and you'll see that the label changed in the map. There's another way to make that same expression using one of the Arcade numeric functions.

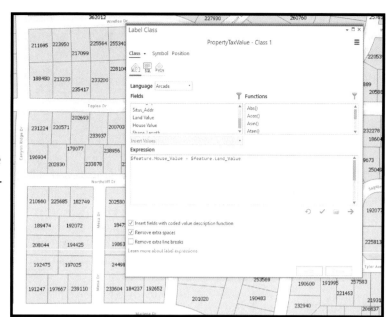

A reference to all the functions available in Arcade is located here:

https://developers.arcgis.com/arcade/function-reference/

… or search for Arcade Function Reference.

You will see that the functions are divided into groups, and for this example scroll down to the Mathematical Functions group. Look for the function **Sum()** and click it to see the reference.

The Sum function can be used to total up multiple values within the same feature using the $feature global variable, but notice that it can also be used to sum the values of all the features in the selected layer using the $layer global variable. For this example, you will just be adding to attribute values within the layer together. The syntax will be to use the **Sum()** function, then list the values separated by commas.

As you work through this book, you will want to research all the commands and functions in this Arcade Reference.

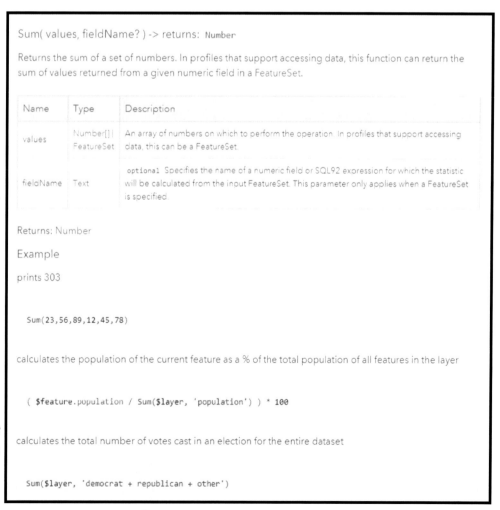

8 Change the expression to *sum($feature.House_Value, $feature.Land_Value)* and click Validate and Apply.

Did you see any changes in the map? If you did, check the expression again because it should produce the exact same results.

This would also look better with a dollar sign in front of the number so that people will understand this represents money. You can add the dollar sign enclosed in single or double quotes to the expression, then adding it to the output of the sum function. What's interesting in Arcade is that it will automatically switch between value types to produce the desired field type. Since a label is expected to be a text string, whatever expression you write is automatically converted to a text string when it is sent to the labeling engine.

9 Add "$" + to the beginning of the expression. Click Validate and Apply. Then close the Label Class pane.

That worked out well, but let's stop for a minute to realize what just happened.

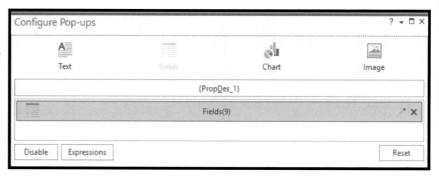

The database doesn't contain a field for total value, so you in effect made one in your expression that will calculate on-the-fly. Even if the values for land and houses are updated, the value returned by your Arcade expression will always be current. Image if you had taken the old-fashioned route and added a field to the table called "TotalVal" and ran the Field Calculator tool to store that value in the new field. Sure, that field could then be used for the label ($feature.TotlVal) but if the land and house values were updated you would have to go recalculate the TotVal field – every time – over and over – forever. Now the Arcade expression will handle it automatically – forever.

> Rafael's Question: It would be really informative if you could build a pop-up that would show a pie chart that showed what percentage of the total value was from the land and what percentage of the total value was from the house. Can that be done? And would it update automatically?

A field showing that percentage doesn't exist, however you could make that with an Arcade expression. The pie chart will show two values. The first will be the house value divided by the total assessed value, and the second will be the land value divided by the total assessed value (with both values multiplied by 100 so that the result shows as a percentage). And since the expression does the calculations on-the-fly, it will be automatically updated if the values changed.

1 In the same project, right click on the layer PropertyTaxValue and select Configure Pop-ups.

By default, the pop-up pane will show a configuration bar for Fields. This is a list of all the fields in the layer, and contains check boxes allowing you to decide which fields are displayed in the pop-up.

You will need to add two new fields (by way of Arcade expressions) to use in the chart. Note that when you create these, each Arcade expression will get a name (using the same rules as a field name with no spaces allowed) and a title (basically a field alias, and spaces are allowed).

2 **Click the Expressions button at the bottom of the pane, then in the Expressions pane click New.**

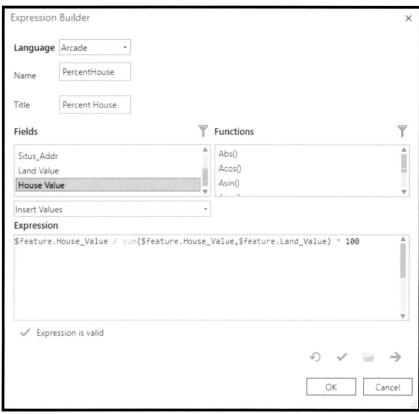

3 **Change the Name to 'PercentHouse' and the Title to 'Percent House'.**

4 **Build the expression to calculate the percentage of the total value represented by the house value (reference the equation above). Click OK.**

5 **Next, click New and build an expression named PercentLand (titled Percent Land) that does the same formatting except with the land value field. Click OK.**

6 **Click the Back arrow to return to the Configure Pop-ups pane.**

You will add a new pie chart and configure it to use the new expressions.

7 Click the Chart  icon .

A new row for the chart is added to the list of items that will be displayed in the pop-up.

8 Click the Edit Pop-up Element icon on the new Chart bar

9 At the top of the pane, click the Pie Chart icon <fig1-14.tif>Add the Caption "Percentage break-down of House and Land value".

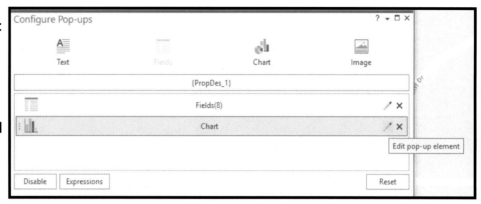

10 In the Fields list, check the boxes next to Percent House and Percent Land.

11 Use the Back button to return to the Configure Pop-ups pane. Note that changes are applied and saved automatically.

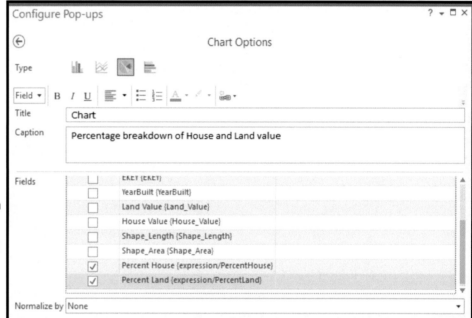

The Fields bar now shows that there are two additional fields being displayed. For this circumstance you will only want the two values involved in the chart calculation displayed, although you could show whichever fields you like.

12 Click the Edit tool on the Fields bar. Uncheck all the fields except House Value and Land Value. Hint: Check then Uncheck Display to turn all the fields off, then check the two fields that you want.

13 All the configurations are completed so click the back arrow, then close the configuration pane.

14 Now click on one of the pieces of property to open the Pop-up. Then click on more and watch the pie chart change.

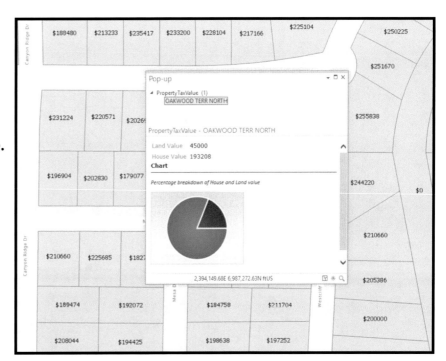

Note that the pop-up shows all the elements you configured – the two value fields and the pie chard showing the percentage split in the total assessed value. Here's the kicker … no changes were made to the database schema AT ALL to accommodate what in effect is three new attribute values. And Rafael – YES they are up-dated automatically when the house or land values are updated.

In the pop-up configuration pane, once you made a new expression that expression could be used anywhere in the pane. It could be the pop-up title, a field to display, used in a text or chart display … whatever you want.

On your own

After the boss looked at this, she commented that nowhere in the pop-up window is the total assessed value shown. Oops! Go back to the Pop-up Configuration and add the total assessed value as the title of the chart. Hint: make a new expression for TotValue, then highlight the Title bar in the Chart configuration and select your new field. Click on a bunch of property in the map to test it and see the charts and values change.

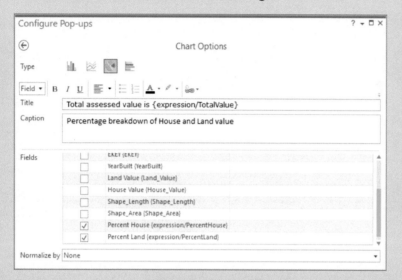

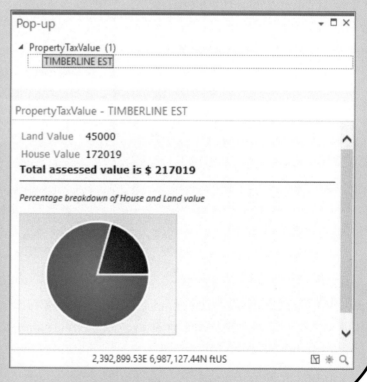

Chapter 2 —Using Arcade Functions

Placing functions in your expressions and managing the results

You got a small taste of using functions in your Arcade script with **Sum()**, and now is a good time to look at the full selection of functions to see how they are used. The functions are grouped in several categories, and if you are familiar with other programming languages you will recognize the categories of Mathematical Functions, Text Functions, Date Functions, and Logical Functions. When writing expressions, you are also able to filter the display of the function list by the categories. This is helpful when you are, for example, looking for a particular mathematical function and want to see only that category of functions. Or likewise you may want to see only the text functions. No sense wading through the long list when many of the functions won't even work on text.

Mathematical functions will act upon a numeric field, value, or variable, and return the calculated value. These include common functions like Sum (which you just used), Average (returns the average of the supplied values), Max (returns the maximum of the supplied values), Mean (returns the mean of the supplied values), Min (returns the minimum of the supplied values), Round (rounds the value up to a specified number of decimal places), and Sqrt (calculates the square root of the supplied values). Most everyone is familiar with how these are used and what value to expect them to return. Other less traditional functions include the sine, cosine, tangent, arctangent, sine, cosine, absolute value, and others. These all perform a calculation and return a number. Become familiar with these functions and use the description in the function reference to learn the actual syntax of their use.

Text functions are also pretty familiar to most programmers and deal with the formatting and appearance of text strings. These are used to manipulate a text string (sometimes character by character) and return another text string that can be used as a label, an alias, or even a value for symbol classifications. Note that Arcade indexes the characters in a string starting with 0 (zero). So the first character in a sting is index number 0, the second is 1, the third is 2, and so on. You'll see later how to use these index values. Functions such as Count, Find, and Mid will use or return these index numbers that you can reference to manipulate text. Other functions such as Upper, Lower, Proper, Left, Right, and Trim can change the capitalization and remove unwanted blank spaces in a text string.

Date functions are probably the hardest to understand and work with, and this is due partly to the complex nature of date fields and values. A date value can contain numbers representing the time, the date, the month, and the year, but can also be formatted to show these values in other ways, such as military time or text descriptions for day of the week, or name of the month. All of these separate values can be extracted from a single date value. A variety of functions can be used to determine things like the time elapsed between two dates, convert between time zones, or even add time to an existing date value.

And the last of the standard function categories is Logical Functions. These include the Boolean function (returns a true or false) and the ever popular **Iif** statement (evaluate a value against a condition and return one of two choices). Note that there is no Else statement with the **Iif** in Arcade, so you can't nest **Iif** statements. There is, however, a When function that can evaluate a series of conditional expressions until one becomes true – the same way you would do with If/Else statements. Many of these are similar to the logic used in other programming languages with just a few tweaks so it's important to understand how they are used.

By the way, if you thought you were going to get through Arcade without learning to program, you were wrong. This IS a true programming language, albeit for expressions rather than stand-alone applications.

These first few categories are functions that you probably have seen in other programming languages. However, the last two groups of functions are more specific to working with spatial data. These are the Data Functions and the Geometry Functions. The lists here are too long to go over one by one, but many will be highlighted in the upcoming exercises.

Formatting text

The next exercise will use some of the text formatting functions to reformat an owner-name field from a dataset. The possibility always exists that you could create a new field in the layer's attribute table and calculate a properly formatted string into that field … but again you are adding a maintenance step for all future uses of this map. Instead you will write an Arcade expression to redo all the formatting (Yes, Rafael … on-the-fly, automatically, forever and ever, blah blah blah).

You will also pay attention to the number of lines your expression uses. When an Arcade expression is run, each query of the data requires that the script pull all the data into memory, perform that operation, then release the data. If you have three queries on three separate lines, the data is retrieved into memory three times before the expression is completed. This won't be a big deal on desktop uses, but in web apps you will want to minimize the number of times the data must be queried. If all of the queries can be built into a single line expression, the data is retrieved only once, all the evaluation is done, and the data is released. In these exercises you will first build these using multiple lines, then try to minimize the number of lines by making your expression more succinct and trying to get it all on one line. By the way, comments have no effect on the speed or efficiency of your expression.

Exercise 2 – Formatting the owner name data

The property data provided comes from the regional taxing district and contains the owner's name in one field, and the owner's address in another. It is updated every month but is formatted rather oddly. The owner name field will typically have the last name, then a comma, then the first name, then a Latin abbreviation ETUX (meaning "and wife") or ETAL (meaning "and others"). After that comes the first name and middle initial of the co-owner.

Many times the planning office has to mail out legal notices to property owners so they want to format this and make it easier to read and understand, and avoid accidently mailing letters to Mr. Etux.

1 **Start ArcGIS Pro and open Exercise 2 and move to the Area 1 bookmark, if necessary.**

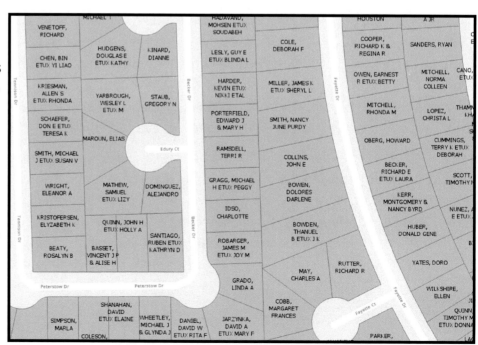

The Property Ownership layer has labels turned on and is using the field OWNER_NAME. That's the correct field from the tax department table, it's just not formatted very well. You can see that several of the names have an ampersand in them (these are newer records) but many still have the Latin abbreviation ETUX. All of the fields follow the format of:

Last Name / Comma / First Name / Middle Initial / ETUX / First Name of co-owner / Middle Initial of co-owner

The desired output would be:

First Name / Middle Initial / & / First Name of co-owner / Middle Initial of co-owner / Last Name

Using this formula, the unformatted text string:

Allen, David W ETUX Holly H

Becomes this more readable formatted string:

David W & Holly H Allen

The strategy will be to first isolate the last name which will be all of the characters to the left of the comma. This can be done by using **Find()** to locate the index position of the comma, then **Left()** to extract everything to the left of the comma's location. Check these functions in the Arcade Function Reference to see the syntax and an example.

2 **Highlight the property Ownership layer, click the labeling tab, and in the Label Class area open the Expression pane. Delete the current expression.**

Type var *CommaLoc* = to start the variable definition.

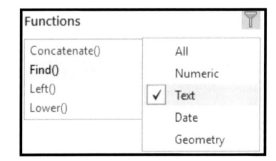

3 **Above the Fields list, click the Filter icon and select Text.**

4 **Scroll down and double click the Find() function. The syntax of this function is to provide the character you are looking for, then the field in which to look. There is an option to specify where to start looking, but the default is character 0 (the left) and that's what you want.**

5 After the first parenthesis, add ",". Then type a comma, and finally double click OWNER_NAME in the Fields list. Validate the expression.

The CommaLoc variable will be the index number of the location of the comma. Everything to the left of that comma is the last name. Using **Left()** you can start at the left and extract everything until you reach the comma location.

Expression

```
var CommaLoc = Find(",",$feature['TaxRecords2019.OWNER_NAME'])
```

✓ Expression is valid

6 In the next line, type *var Lastname = .* Add the Left() function from the Functions list. The syntax of this function is to provide the field name, then the number of characters to extract.

7 Place the cursor between the parentheses and double click the field OWNER_NAME. Then add a comma, and finally type *CommaLoc*. Validate the expression.

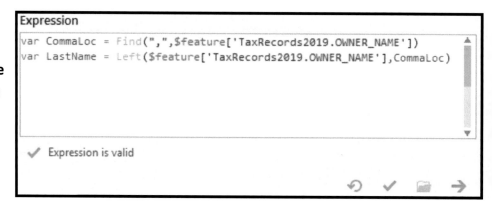

Expression

```
var CommaLoc = Find(",",$feature['TaxRecords2019.OWNER_NAME'])
var LastName = Left($feature['TaxRecords2019.OWNER_NAME'],CommaLoc)
```

✓ Expression is valid

OK – there's the first part. Next is to get the first name of the two owners. That's basically all the text to the right of the comma – but remember that you will want to start one character over from the comma location. The **Mid()** function can do this (check the syntax in the Arcade Function Reference). For the last parameter, use 25 as the number of characters to extract. That should suffice for all occurrences.

8 Add the line *var FirstName = Mid($feature['TaxRecords2019.OWNER_NAME'], CommaLoc+1, 25)* and validate the expression.

The names are property split now, but the Latin phrase ETUX will still be in some of them. The **Replace()** function can change that to the word 'and'. Research the syntax for the **Replace()** function.

Expression

```
var CommaLoc = Find(",",$feature['TaxRecords2019.OWNER_NAME'])
var LastName = Left($feature['TaxRecords2019.OWNER_NAME'],CommaLoc)
var FirstName = Mid($feature['TaxRecords2019.OWNER_NAME'],CommaLoc+1,25)
```

✓ Expression is valid

9 **Amend the FirstName variable to include the Replace() function.**

Note that when the line got too long for the dialog box, it jumped to a new line and a small icon was added to indicate that the line continues.

```
Expression
var CommaLoc = Find(",",$feature['TaxRecords2019.OWNER_NAME'])
var LastName = Left($feature['TaxRecords2019.OWNER_NAME'],CommaLoc)
var FirstName = Replace(Mid($feature['TaxRecords2019.OWNER_NAME'],CommaLoc
+1,25),'ETUX','and')
```

✓ Expression is valid

The last step is to combine the LastName variable and FirstName variable into a single text string. This could be done on the last line and by default it will be the Return line – that is the value will be used for the label. It might also be good to apply a formatting function so that all the words will be the same, instead of a random use of upper and lower case letters. Check the available functions … here you will use the **Proper()** function but you may try others to see if you like the results better.

10 **On the last line, add the command to combine the two variables with a space in between along with the Proper function. Validate the express, then click Apply to see the results in the map.**

Excellent work! That looks so much better.

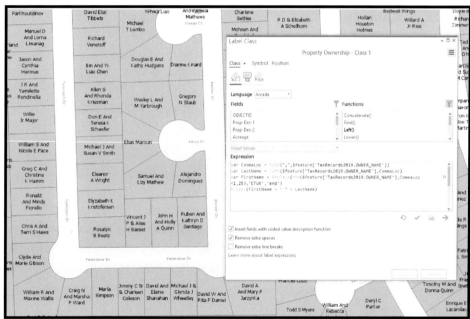

Rafael's Question: How many queries does this make to the database? Shouldn't we try to reduce that to a single line if possible? How would I do that?

Yes, ideally you want the Arcade expression to be on a single line. Sometimes this isn't possible, but most of the time you can get your expression down to just a few lines. The way to do this would be to copy/paste the expression for each variable and place that in place of the variable name everywhere it occurs. In this instance, the expression for CommaLoc will be placed inside the expression for both the FirstName and Last-Name variables. Then those new expressions will be used in place of the variable names in the return line. This will result in one concise line that will perform this entire formatting process with only one query of the dataset. Try it on your own first, then check against the image on the next page.

11 Make the appropriate changes to get the entire expression on one line. Note that even as the expression gets longer it will automatically wrap within the pane and add the icon showing that the expression continues on the next line. This image shows the original expression commented out, and the new expression at the bottom.

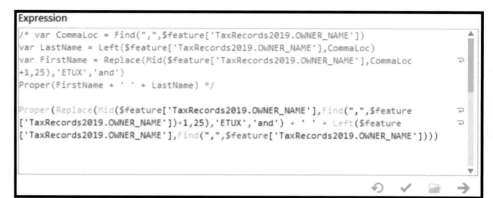

12 Save and close the project.

As you see, that last expression was VERY complex, and it's doubtful that anyone could write that expression first without working through the steps as you did. Feel free to build them in pieces, check them as you go, and after the expression is providing the correct results you can work on making it more concise. It's also helpful to keep the original multi-line code as a comment in your expression for future reference.

Rafael's Question—Can I save my Arcade expressions and use them in other projects?

Yes! The expression building dialog includes both an Export and Import button. The file is saved with an .LXP extension, which stands for Label Expression. And despite it having the word label in the name, it saves any expression even if it's used in a chart or for controlling symbology.

Chapter 3—Using Arcade in ArcGIS Online

Accessing the profiles in online web maps

Your first introduction into using Arcade used simple syntax and functions. Now you will find that when you use Arcade with your online mapping there is no change in how you make your expressions. You might see some differences in the dialog boxes, but the code you write will be identical.

This next exercise won't introduce any new code elements, but rather just introduce you to the process of adding Arcade to your online maps. You should have your own ArcGIS Online (AGOL) account with permissions to add new maps. Again, this book isn't about using ArcGIS Online so if you are not familiar with navigating through its menus please start with tutorials that will get you familiar with it.

Exercise 3 – Using Arcade online

The boss has asked you to make a map showing some specific population demographics that will be shown to the board of directors. They all get an electronic packet for meetings, so the best platform for building the display will be through AGOL. You will also need to use some data from the Esri Living Atlas that can provide the necessary population numbers. Note also that the data won't be editable and you won't be able to add any fields.

1 Open a browser and log in to your ArcGIS Online account.

2 Move to the Contents tab and select Create > Map.

3 Add a title, Tags, and Summary for the new map as shown and click OK.

4 **When the new map opens, click Add > Browse Living Atlas layers.**

The Living Atlas contains GIS data that can be used within AGOL – much of it from users like you and much of it for free. Layers marked Authoritative are regularly updated and are contributed but the primary authority for that data, and layers marked Premium require an ArcGIS Online organizational account and will consume credits.

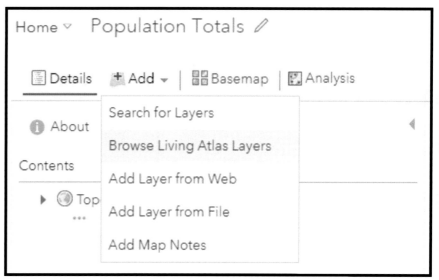

5 **In the search box, type USA Census Populated Places. Click the Plus sign at the lower right of the layer name to add it to your map. When the layer is added, click the left arrow to return to the main Details pane.**

The data will appear in your map. You can zoom it to anywhere in the US that you like or are familiar with. In the examples, the map is zoomed in to Birmingham, Alabama, showing the Opossum Valley.

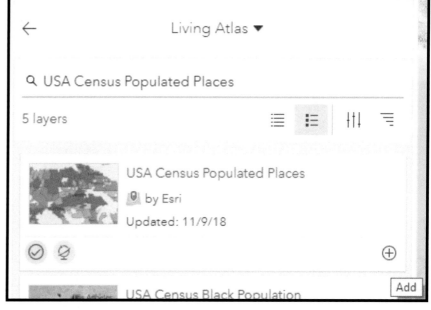

The first step will be to add a label to the map showing the housing density – that's the number of houses divided by the area in square miles. You will use the fields Housing Units and Sq.Mi. in an arcade expression to get the value to display.

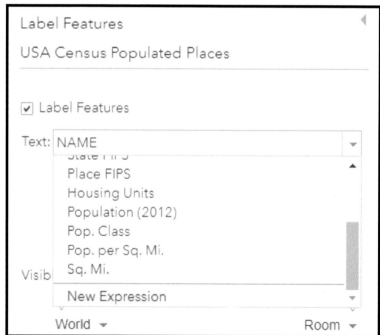

6 Click the layer name USA Census Populated Places to show the menu bar, then click the Options icon and select Create Labels.

7 Click the Text drop-down list. All the existing fields are shown. Scroll to the bottom of the list and select New Expression.

The dialog that opens will accomplish the same thing as the desktop dialogs ... it just looks different. The Arcade code will be the same as you would write in any other profile.

This label expression will be pretty simple. It will be the field Housing Units divided by the field Sq. Mi. You may also want to add some unit description to the end of the string. Fields are added to the expression by clicking the blue text name of the field.

8 **Add the expression as shown in the graphic, then press the Test button.**

Rafael's Question - Why is mine broken? I didn't get it to work!

A quick look shows that there is an issue with the code that Rafael typed. There's a red error box in the left column showing that this line has an error, and when pausing over the box you can see that there is an unex-pected token. After glancing over the code you can see that he didn't close the double quotes around the text string that he is adding to the results. If he were to add the double quotes the error box would disappear and the code would test correctly.

The test shows what the displayed value will be, but there's WAAAYYY too many digits past the decimal point. One would be sufficient. Perhaps there's a way to round the number off to one decimal place.

9 **Click the Functions tab and enter round. The function Round() is found – click the information button to show the description and syntax for this function.**

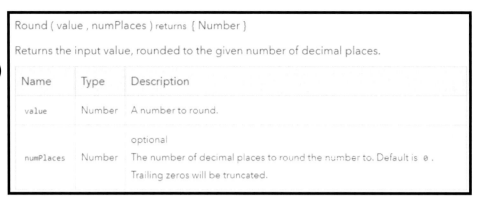

Round (value , numPlaces) returns { Number }

Returns the input value, rounded to the given number of decimal places.

Name	Type	Description
value	Number	A number to round.
numPlaces	Number	optional The number of decimal places to round the number to. Default is 0 . Trailing zeros will be truncated.

10 **Try modifying the expression to include the Round() function on your own first before looking at the answer below.**

```
1   Round($feature.HOUSEUNITS / $feature.SQMI,1) + " units per sq mi"
```

11 **Test the expression again and see if your code worked.**

Result	Value
Result	61.5 units per sq mi

12 **If your expression worked, click OK to return to the Label Features pane. You will notice that your new expression is now the label field in the Text box.**

13 **To make the labels more visible, make them bold, italic, and add a 3 point halo. Then click OK.**

Pan around a bit and you can see that the values display for every area – automatically updated and forever ... ok, you know I'm tired of saying that. Even Rafael gets it by now.

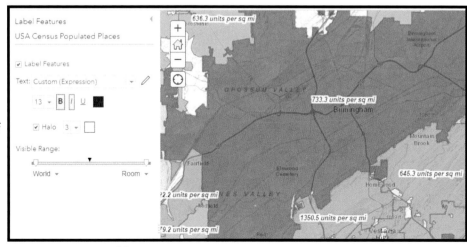

Expanding the expression

Next you need to show the directors the ratio between the number of residents that commute out of an area vs. the number of workers that commute into an area. The total population count from the Census represents the number of people who live in the Census tract. If you subtract the number of residents that remain in the area, the result is the number of people who commuted out. Then you can compare that with the number of daytime workers. This can be valuable information when planning the size of police forces and fire departments. Many urban downtown areas have a small overnight population but a large number of commuting workers during the day. The need for police and fire are greater during the day than in the evenings – whereas this scenario might be reversed in a suburb where people commute to downtown during the day.

There is a Living Atlas layer with this data called USA 2016 Daytime Population. It contains a field TOTPOP_CY (Total Population) and a breakdown of daytime population between residents (DPOPRES_CY) and workers (DPOPWRK_CY). The total population minus the daytime population of residents will represent the number of people commuting to another area. Since there is no existing field with this value you will have to create an expression to do it. Once you figure out how to calculate these values, you will create a pie chart in the pop-up display.

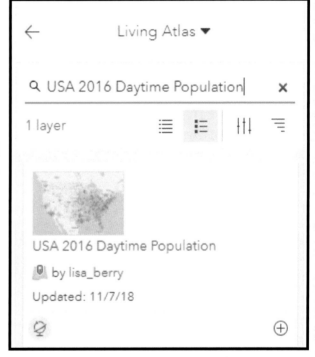

1 **Browse the Living Atlas again, find the layer USA 2016 Daytime Population, and add it to your map.**

Three new layers are added, each representing the data at the Census tract, county, and state levels. You are interested only in the Census tract level and can turn the other two layers off.

2 **Uncheck the Daytime Population layers for State and County.**

In your map you can see the new layer. The daytime population data is shown as red and blue triangle of different sizes. The larger the triangle, the larger the daytime population. And the color blue represents areas where the daytime population is less than the total population and red represents the reverse case where the daytime population exceeds the total population. That's interesting data, but we want to show the ratio between commuters and workers.

Also if you click one of the symbols you will see that the pop-up already has a pie chart in it. It is showing the split of population between daytime workers and daytime residents using two supplied fields. We don't want that so we'll take that pie chart out of the pop-up.

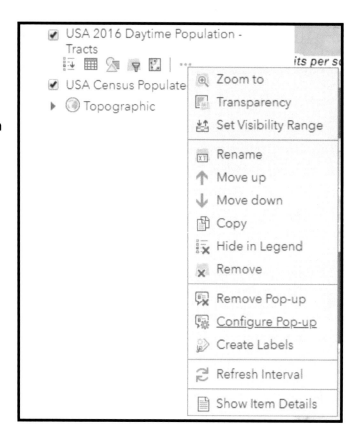

3 Click the layer name to expose the menu bar, then click the options button. Select Configure Pop-up.

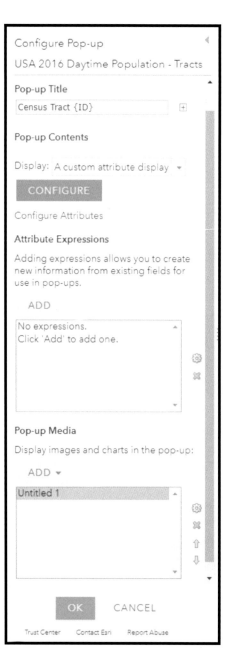

The middle part of the Configure Pop-up pane has an area called Attribute Expressions. This is where you will build the expression to calculate the commuter population.

The bottom part of the Configure Pop-up pane has an area called Pop-up Media which is where images and charts are displayed. The entry Untitled 1 is the existing chart, which will be removed.

4 In the Attribute Expression area, click Add.

You should recognize the Custom pane and its contents with one difference. Because this dataset included several layers you will now see the variable prefixes $feature, and $layer which were discussed earlier. The prefix $feature references values from individual features in the layer while $layer references the total values within the layer.

5 At the top of the pane click the Edit pencil icon next to the word Custom and change the title to *Commuter_Pop*, then click Save. This will be the name of the expression.

6 Next move to the Globals pane and click the blue arrow to the right of $feature. This will expand the list of attributes within the layer.

7 Build the expression shown here, then click Test. If the expression tests out to be valid, click OK to close the pane.

Next you will remove the existing pie chart and make a new one using the fields Daytime Population: Workers and Commuter_Pop.

8 Move to the Pop-up Media area. Highlight the entry Untitled 1, then click the X to remove it.

9 Next click the Add button and select Pie Chart.

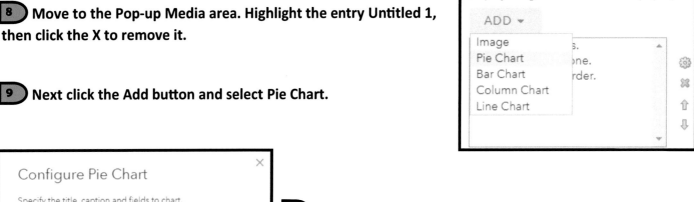

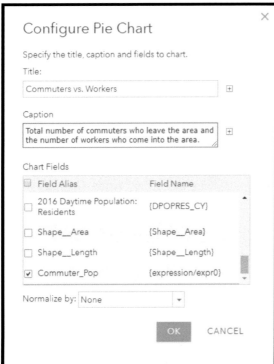

10 In the Configure Pie Chart pane check the box next to the fields 2016 Daytime Population: Workers and Commuter_Pop. Add a title and caption and click OK.

11 Click OK to close the Configure Pop-up pane.

12 Save the map.

24

13 **Now test the pop-up display by selecting several of the points from the USA Daytime Population Tracts layer. Each point will display your custom pie chart.**

Just like the desktop profile, you made a label and configured a pop-up chart using custom Arcade expressions. As you discovered, the syntax and components of the code are the same.

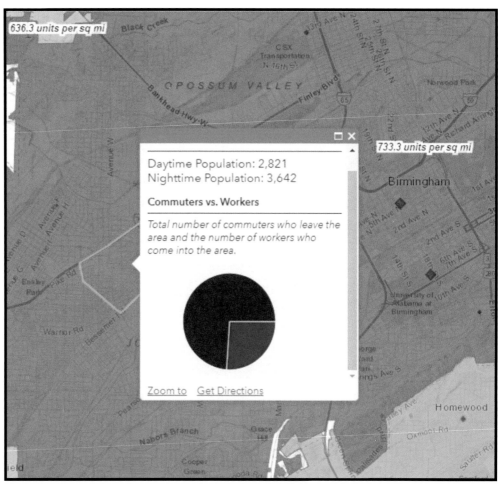

14 **Save your map and log out of ArcGIS Online.**

Making a web map from a Project

Now for the ultimate test ... if you share a map you made in ArcGIS Pro as a web map it should take the custom labels and pop-up with it. In fact, anything you set up using Arcade will transition seamlessly to AGOL. Or at least that's what they tell us! You can try this out with the project you completed in Exercise 1.

Exercise 4 – Making a web map with an Arcade Expression included

If you recall, this project has a custom label showing the property value and a custom pie chart showing the percentage split between land value and house value. You will share this single layer and display it in a web map to see what happens.

1 Start ArcGIS Pro and open your completed Exercise 1 project file.

2 Make sure you are logged in to your ArcGIS Online account. In this example the author made a new folder called Arcade Scripts to store any of the work from this book. You may go into the Contents tab of your AGOL account and do the same before sharing the layer but it is not necessary.

3 Right-click the Property Tax Value layer and select Sharing > Share as Web Layer.

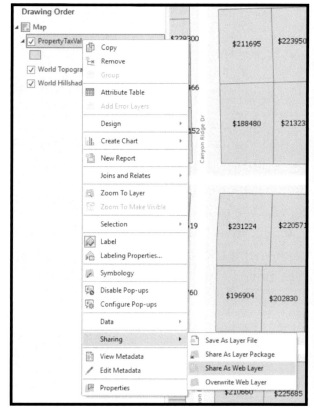

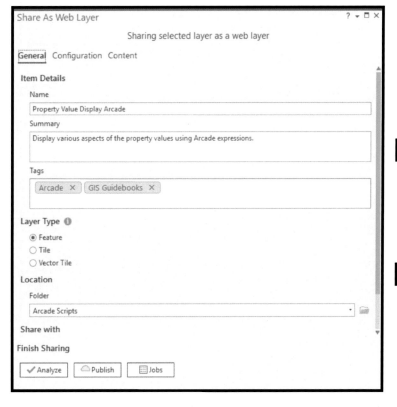

4 Name the layer Property Value Display Arcade, and give it an appropriate description and tags. Note that the image is showing the file is going into the special folder.

5 Click Analyze and check for any issues. If none are found, click Publish. When the process finishes, save and close the project.

26

6 Open and log in to your ArcGIS Online account. Move to the folder (if any) where you stored the layer.

7 Click the Options button and select Add to new map.

The map will open and ask that you set up the symbology – which you can close. This example uses a single symbol for all features (it doesn't really matter because all you want to see is the label and pie chart).

Click on one of the properties. You can already see that the property has the total value shown as a label, and you can also see the pie chart showing the breakdown of house vs. land value.

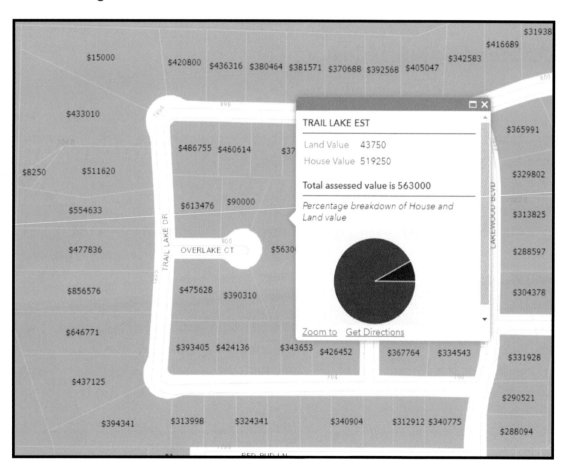

Absolutely no modifications were needed to make this work. In this instance you made a single web layer. That was to demonstrate that the raw data layer carries the arcade expressions with it. You could also have shared the project as a Web map and all the symbology would have also been transferred to AGOL.

On Your Own

Open the Label Features pane in AGOL and check the expression used to label the parcels. Do you see any differences in the Arcade code?

Next, open the Configure Pop-up pane. Check for the Attribute Expressions and the Pop-up Media that use Arcade expressions.

8 **Save the map and log out of AGOL.**

It's important to note that the association between the project layer and the AGOL web layer is not permanent. Each will reside independently in their own space, and could be modified without affecting each other. The best practice here would be to make any changes to the project file, then share the layer to AGOL again, overwriting the existing layer. In this instance you would want to be sure to share only the layer or else you could disturb the symbology and potentially other layers in the web map.

Chapter 4 Building Custom Equations

Controling symbology in a map with Arcade

As you saw with the labeling examples, it is quite often the case that the dataset doesn't contain the field you need to accomplish your goal. It would have been helpful to have a properly formatted owner name field for labeling, but even though it didn't exist in the dataset you were able to make this happen without creating a new field.

The same can be true for symbology. If the field you need isn't there, you can write an Arcade expression to create it. This is especially helpful when you don't have write permissions to the data, and couldn't make a new field if you wanted to. In this first example, you will use local data but in the next you will use online data from the Esri Living Atlas (which is not editable).

In this scenario, you have a dataset with historic property values from several years, including 2018 and 2019. You would like to color code the data to show which properties increased in value, which decreased, and which stayed the same … and of course you'll show varying degrees of change in each direction. There isn't a field containing the percent change and since this data links into the appraisal software you really aren't at liberty to add one. Instead you will make the value on-the-fly and use it in the symbology generator.

The formula for percent changes is to subtract the previous year's value from the current year's value, divide the result by the previous year's value, and multiple that result by 100 to make it a percentage. As a formula, it looks like this:

*(New Value – Old Value) / Old Value * 100*

In the provided dataset the field names are Value 2019 and Value 2018, making the formula:

*(Value2019 – Value2018) / Value 2018 * 100*

Once you get the formula working you will symbolize in seven categories showing no change, 0 to 10% change, 10 to 20% change, and over 20% change (in both the positive and negative directions). If you are unfamiliar with setting a manual classification, check for online tutorials on how to do this.

Exercise 5 – Using an Arcade expression to set symbology

In this exercise you will build expressions in the symbology profile. You will see that the format and syntax are the same as in other profiles.

1 **Start ArcGIS Pro and Open Exercise 5.**

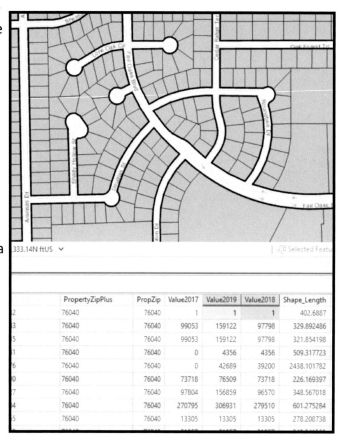

You may want to review the symbology and data fields for the Property Values layer. The data is displayed with a single symbol, and you will see the two value fields mentioned above.

	PropertyZipPlus	PropZip	Value2017	Value2019	Value2018	Shape_Length
2	76040	76040	1	1	1	402.6887
3	76040	76040	99053	159122	97798	329.892486
5	76040	76040	99053	159122	97798	321.854198
1	76040	76040	0	4356	4356	509.317723
6	76040	76040	0	42689	39200	2438.101782
0	76040	76040	73718	76509	73718	226.169397
7	76040	76040	97804	156859	96570	348.567018
4	76040	76040	270795	306931	279510	601.275284
5	76040	76040	13305	13305	13305	278.208738

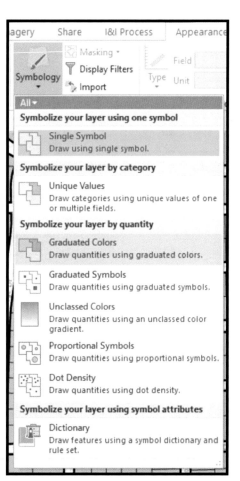

2 **With the Property Values layer highlighted click Appearance, then click the drop-down arrow under Symbology. Select Graduated Colors.**

Any of these symbol classification types uses an attribute to control the symbology. An Arcade expression can be written for any of these and control symbol size, style, classification settings, color, or rotation.

29

3 In the Symbology pane, click the **Expression icon to the right of the Field value.**

You will recognize the Expression format as being Arcade! In the Expression box you will make two variables to hold the values, perform the calculation, and return a value to the symbology generator.

4 Add Arcade code to make two variables for NewValue and OldValue (Value 2019 and Value2018 respectively).

5 Next, add a variable called PercentChange and set it to equal the calculation outlined above.

6 Finally, add the Return statement to send the results to the symbology generator. Validate the expression before clicking OK.

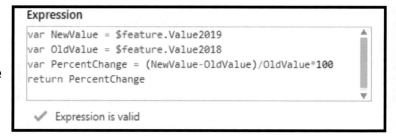

Rafael's Question – Can I try to simplify that expression?

Of course! The examples shown here are often a bit verbose so that you can better see all the steps, but at any time you are welcome to try and simplify the expression. Always validate the expression before continuing, and make sure it is accomplishing the same goal.

Did you get this?

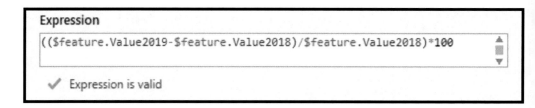

The expression is now controlling the symbology. You should have gotten the default Natural Breaks classification with 5 classes. These next steps are merely to set the symbology – forge ahead on your own if you are comfortable with this process, or follow these steps.

7 Change the number of classes to 7.

8 Change the symbology method to Manual Interval.

9 Change the Upper Value column to match below (HINT: pause the map refresh, then change the values starting at the top and moving down.

Upper value ▲
≤ -44.81159
≤ -20.0
≤ -10.0
≤ 0.0
≤ 10.0
≤ 20.0
≤ 981.582402

10 Change the Color Scheme to the red to green gradation. Unpause your refresh (if necessary) and close the Symbology pane. (HINT: You may need to click "Show All" in the palette selection to find the correct scheme)

You can pan around the map (check out the Area 2 and Area 3 bookmarks) to see the values around the city. Remember that these are being generated on the fly from your Arcade expression!

Rafael's Question – What causes some of them to change value drastically, and why are some areas blank?

Remember that these are based on market value estimates. In this area, a large amount of commercial property was added, driving the market values down. You may also see a house on Ducket Dr (Area 2) that dropped in value dramatically because the house burned down. Areas with no color are probably new construction and didn't exist in the prior year so there was no value to compare against. The area on Grace Ave (Area 3) was just constructed in 2019.

Controlling symbology in ArcGIS Online

The last exercise used an Arcade expression to control the symbology in an ArcGIS Pro project, and this next one will control symbology in ArcGIS Online. You again will see slight differences in the interface but the expressions work the same way. There are some layers in the Esri Living Atlas that can be used to demonstrate this technique.

Exercise 6 – Control symbology in online data

For this scenario, you have been asked by a political support group to look at how the total number of rental properties might change between 2016 and 2021. It is known that people who rent residential space (apartments or houses) tend to be less politically active in local and regional elections (mayors, city council members, district judges, school board members, etc…) and this political group wants to start an advertising campaign to inform renters about the importance of voting. But they want to target their efforts in areas where they think the number of renters will increase.

The Esri Living Atlas contains a feature layer called *2017 Population Density by Congressional District* that also contains the demographic data you need, although it doesn't have a field with the exact value you wish to highlight. Once you locate the data in the atlas you can open a map viewer and set the symbology using an Arcade Expression.

1 **Open a web browser and go to https://LivingAtlas.Arcgis.com. Search for '2016 Population Density by Congressional District'.**

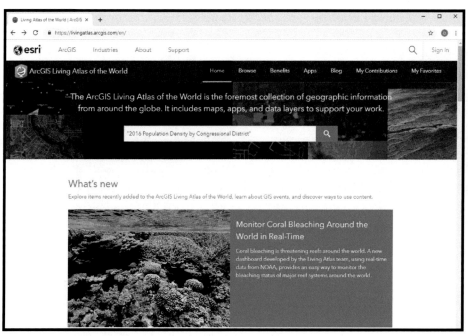

2 At the far right of the layer listing, click the ellipsis button and select Map Viewer (you may be asked to log in with your ArcGIS Online account).

3 In the Contents pane select Change Style, then click the drop down selection under *Choose an attribute to show*.

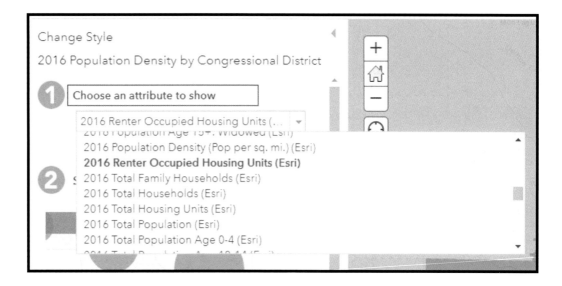

If you look down this list you will see fields containing a very large number of demographic categories, including 2016 Renter Occupied Housing Units and 2021 Renter Occupied Housing Units. You will also see a range of individual fields showing the growth rate in many of the categories. When this data was created in 2016 (before Arcade was invented) the only way to show the growth rates was to add a field and calculate a new value. They did this for many of the categories, but they a) couldn't do all of the categories and b) couldn't begin to approach all the cross reference analysis that every GIS user in the world would want. So they limited themselves to just a few … and didn't calculate the growth rate of rental units. But you know something that they didn't know back then … how to build that calculation on the fly with Arcade.

Rafael's Question—We learned how to calculate the percent change in property values … how does that relate to the count of rental units?

The formula to calculate the percent change is the same as what you used earlier – and in fact is the same for any two value categories:

*(New Value – Old Value) / Old Value * 100*

… or in this case …

*(2021 Rental Units – 2016 Rental Units) / 2016 Rental Units * 100*

4 **Open the Choose Attribute to Show list again, scroll all the way to the bottom, and select New Expression.**

The Custom > Expression pane will open. This will look a little different than in ArcGIS Pro, but you will build the expression the same way – first the long way, then you can shorten it if you like (shown as a comment below).

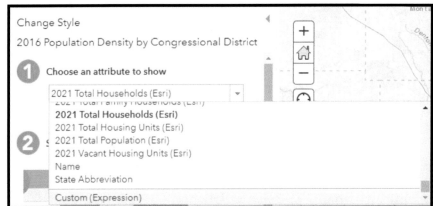

5 **Build the expression using the two Renter Occupied Housing fields, and test that it is valid. (HINT: In ArcGIS Online the Validate button is called Test).**

6 **Click OK, then click Count and Amounts (Color).**

If you are familiar with setting symbology in AGOL, go ahead and set up a similar manual classification with -2, 0, 2, and up. If you aren't familiar with this, just move on knowing that the values are being calculated on the fly for you.

7 **Click OK and Done.**

According to this analysis, your "Get out and Vote" campaigns targeting the growing rental population should be focused on the medium and dark green areas.

You saw that the online functionality of Arcade was identical to the desktop functionality – in fact you could copy/paste that same formula to the desktop and it would work with no changes. One thing you did notice was that it was harder to set up the classification online. An alternative workflow would be to build this using the Living Atlas data in desktop ArcGIS Pro, then share it as a web layer so that the desktop symbology and classification will go with it.

Chapter 5—Using Logic in Arcade

The Arcade logic functions can be used to control the expression

Any programming language you study will include some form of logic functions. You saw the Arcade logic functions mentioned earlier, and you can review them on the ArcGIS for Developers Arcade reference.

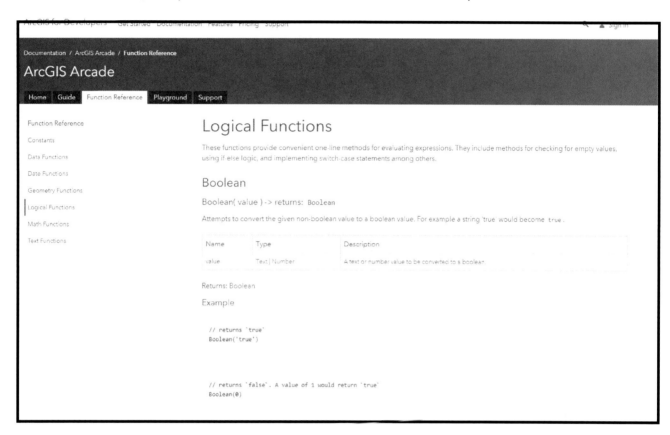

When most non-programmers think of programming logic, they think of two main functions – If/Then/Else and Boolean. The Arcade Iif() function presents some statement or expression (called a condition) and if the condition resolves to True, a certain course of action is taken. If the condition resolves to False, a different course of action is taken. The condition can be any expression you write, any variable that may be returned by another function, a value from a field in the dataset, or any number of these types of expressions provided that they can be resolved to either *True* or *False*. The format of the condition used with an if statement is generally ***Expression - Operator - Value***. You can review the operators in the Arcade reference, but the most common are greater than (>), less than (<), or equates to (==). And of course, you also get greater than or equal to, and less than or equal to (>= and <=). For example if I wanted to color code high rent vs. low rent (with $1500 being the median) my condition would be "RentCost > 1500" with the action being "color red". Everything that didn't meet this condition would have the action "color green". The results of this condition can always resolve to True or False – two choices.

The single equals sign is used to assign a value to a variable. So if you wanted to store a property ID number in a variable you would format that as:

var PropID = 53221

The variable is assigned the specified value.

The double equals sign means "equates to" and is a test used in a condition statement to see if two values are the same. An example in a logic statement might be:

SelectedPropertyID == PropID

You could read this as "does the selected property ID equate to the stored property ID" and the result would be either True or False.

In Arcade the **Iif()** function contains a condition statement, the value to return if the condition resolves to True, and the value to return if the condition is resolved to False.

Iif(condition, TrueValue,FalseValue)

Using the example above, you could build this statement:

Iif(RentCost>1500, "High", "Low")

This might be to place one of two labels on a building, or to supply a value to a unique value renderer for symbology.

Note: the Iif function in Arcade is an upper case I, a lower case i, and a lower case f. Different fonts may make this appear to contain various other letters. Check the Arcade Function Reference for any clarifications.

Exercise 7 – Using the Iif() function in symbology

To try out some IF logic, you will color code some property based on whether or not it is owner occupied. And as you may have already guessed, there's no field with this value in it. The supplied dataset has the address of the property and the address of the owner. If these are the same, the owner probably lives on the property. If they are different, the owner probably lives somewhere else and rents this property. Notice that it fits the requirements of the **Iif()** function by having a condition and two possible actions.

1 **Start ArcGIS Pro and open Exercise 7. It's the familiar property dataset with a definition query to show only residential property.**

The data has a field called Situs_Address, representing the address of the property, and Owner_Address, representing the owner's address. You will check to see if these two are the same and symbolize accordingly. (… and before Rafael asks, Situs is Latin for "location or place")

2 **Highlight the Property Data layer and set the symbology to Unique Values. (Hint: Appearance> Symbology)**

You will see the Field 1 line where the attribute is selected that will control the symbology. You instead want to use a value that doesn't exist yet. Use Arcade, on-the-fly, write code, etc…

3 Click the Set An Expression button.

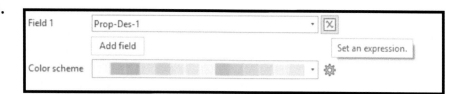

4 In the Expression Builder pane, set the Title to Rental Status.

You will use the fields mentioned above in the condition statement – and remember the format is

Iif(Condition,True,False)

The two output values will be "Owner" if the two values are the same and "Renter" if the values are different.

5 Delete the existing expression and type *Iif(* . Then find the Situs_address field in the Fields list and double click it. Type in ==, then find and double click the Owner_Address field.

6 Next add a comma and type in the two results values. The values will need to be in quotes and separated by a comma. Then add a close parentheses.

7 Verify the expression (fix if needed) and click OK. Set the color if you like, and turn off the Show All Other Values option.

You can see that the map has been categorized by the two values you specified in the **Iif()** statement. In the Contents Pane as well as any legends you might add, the classification field will be shown as the title you gave the expression, and the two classification values will be the two values you put in the **Iif()** statement.

The key to doing this is to make sure that the condition you put in the **Iif()** statement can only have a true or false answer.

On Your Own

Move to the second map in the Exercise 7 project called Atlas Data. This data comes from the Esri Living Atlas of the World. The layer in this map contains a point for the major US cities. The data normally comes symbolized by some sort of population code, but for this task you will symbolize it as a big dot for cities with a population over 1,000,000 and a small dot for cities below that level. Use the Population (2015) field and the condition statement below.

Expression

```
Iif($feature.POPULATION>= 1000000,"Large","Small")
```

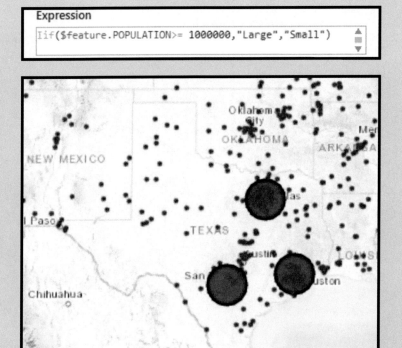

Multi-value logic statements

The **Iif()** statement only allows two outcomes – True or False. But not every condition is a two choice, yes/no equation. What if I wanted to symbolize the city population data in three levels: zero to 250,000; 250,001 to 1 million; and over 1 million. The **Iif()** statement just won't do that. But the **When()** statement will.

There are two things to research in the Arcade Function Reference before you try this. First, go look up the **When()** logical function, then look up the Operators for joining expressions using And and Or.

The format of the **When()** statement is to have a **condition - value** pair for each value you wish to return. In this case we would have three values to return:

Less than 250,000 is Small

Between 250,000 and 1 million is Medium

Over 1 million is Large

There's also an interesting thing about the **When()** statement – you can add a value at the end without a condition that will be used as the default if none of the conditions are True. That makes the statement for three values look like this:

When (Condition1,Value1,Condition2,Value2,Default)

Can you determine what the conditions will be for the three cases shown above? And do you know what Operators to use? If so, continue with the exercise.

Exercise 8—Building a When statement

This scenario will build a statement using the **When()** function with more than two optional outcomes.

1 Start ArcGIS Pro and open Exercise 8. You will see the unsymbolized USA Major Cities layer from the Esri Living Atlas.

2 Open the Symbology Pane for the USA Major Cities layer with the classification set to Unique Values.

3 Click the Set An Expression button and name the expression City Size.

4 Delete the existing code and start by typing When(.

5 Add the first condition for population under 250,000 along with the value "Low" as the outcome.

6 Next, add the condition for the population between 250,000 and 1 million. Make sure to separate the conditions and values with a comma.

```
Expression
When(
$feature.POPULATION <= 250000,"Low",
$feature.POPULATION > 250000 && $feature.POPULATION <= 1000000,"Medium",
```

7 The last value can be set as the default, which would be used if the other two conditions were false. No need to write a condition state, just provide the default value and close with a parentheses. Validate the expression to make sure you have everything entered correctly

```
Expression
When(
$feature.POPULATION <= 250000,"Low",
$feature.POPULATION > 250000 && $feature.POPULATION <= 1000000,"Medium",
"Large")
```

Note that for clarity each condition - value pair was put on a separate line ... the expression didn't care. You could have written it out as one long expression and it would have been wrapped onto multiple lines automatically.

8 Click OK to close the Symbology Pane, then set the symbols to three different size and/or colors to demonstrate the differences in population.

You can see how this was able to make three output values for the symbology using your set conditions. And while this When statement only had three values, it is unlimited in the number of condition-value pairs you set.

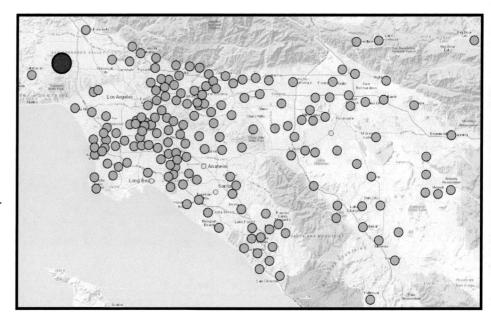

Rafael's Question—Way back in the first exercise we made an expression to label some property data with its value, but it was just displayed as a straight number; for example 233457. It would have looked nicer if we were able to add dollar signs and commas separating the thousands and millions; like this: $233,457. Can that be done with a When statement?

Yes – if you look at it as a series of conditions. If the property value is 999 or less, there are no commas to add. If the value is between 1000 and 999,999 there is only one comma to add – in the 4th position. If the value is between 1,000,000 and 999,999,999 there are two commas to add – in positions 4 and 8. And it's probably not necessary to add a case for property of a billion dollars, but you could set the default to handle it.

There are a few operators you will need to use for text formatting that you haven't used before. If you want to research these, they are the **Mid()**, **Text()**, and **Count()**.

The **Mid()** function allows you to pull characters out of the middle of a string. The format is to provide the string, the index number of where to start, and the number of characters to extract. One tricky thing is that the characters are indexed from the left starting with 0. So a string with four characters would have the index values 0, 1, 2, and 3. All you Python programmers will be used to this already.

The **Text()** will convert a value from any other format into text (called casting). The value can be from an attribute or variable.

Count() simply returns the number of characters in a string. It can also return the number of items in an array or the number of features in a layer – it can be very useful in a number of scenarios and profiles. Note that the field containing the property value is an integer, so you will need to use the **Text()** function to cast it as a string first, then get the count of characters in the string.

Take a look at the description above that gives the breakdowns of when to add a comma. The first instance is when the number of characters has 3 or fewer characters – add no commas. The second is when the number of characters is between 4 and 6 – add one comma. The third is when the number of characters is between 7 and 9 – add two commas. Finally, the last case will be when there are 10 or more characters – add three commas.

Now the part that keeps Rafael up at night. Because you are formatting strings and not numbers, you can't assume that the program will know anything about the 1000's place or the 100,000's place. You are dealing with characters in a string – and the program doesn't even know they are numbers. This means that you will have to build separate condition – value pairs for everything three characters or longer and add commas in the appropriate places. That's a lot of condition – value pairs to build, but you will see that there is some repetition that will make it easier.

1 **Start ArcGIS Pro and open the Property map in Exercise 8. You will see property with values displayed similar to what you had done earlier.**

2 **Click the Labeling tab, then click the Expression button to open the expression builder pane.**

The existing expression can be used for anything 3 characters of shorter, so that can be retained in the first condition – value pair. Since this will be a long and complex expression it will be helpful to build and test these as you go, so you will build two condition – value pairs and test before moving on.

3 Add **When(** to the start of the expression. Next add **Count(Text($feature.Value2019)) <= 3,** to the expression. Finally add **,"Defaut")** so that the When statement will be complete for testing.

4 **Click Apply.**

```
Expression
When(Count(Text($feature.Value2019)) <= 3,"$" + $feature.Value2019,
"DEFAULT")
```

The values should all display DEFAULT except a few of the ROW properties that were values at $1. The next condition will be for values with 4 characters. It will need to use the **Mid()** function to add a comma after the first character (remember you are counting characters starting with index 0 at the left). You will extract the first character by itself, then add a comma, then extract the next three character.

5 Add the condition statement:

Count(Text($feature.Value2019)) == 4,

6 Next, add the value that will be returned:

"$" + Mid($feature.Value2019,0,1) + "," + Mid($feature.Value2019,1,3),

The next two conditions are exactly the same except that they will look for 5 or 6 characters, and extract more characters with the **Mid()** function.

7 Copy/Paste the condition – value pair for 4 characters, and modify them to handle 5 and 6 characters.

```
Expression
When(Count(Text($feature.Value2019)) <= 3,"$" + $feature.Value2019,
Count(Text($feature.Value2019)) == 4,"$" + Mid($feature.Value2019,0,1) + "," + Mid($feature.Value2019,1,3),
Count(Text($feature.Value2019)) == 5,"$" + Mid($feature.Value2019,0,2) + "," + Mid($feature.Value2019,2,3),
Count(Text($feature.Value2019)) == 6,"$" + Mid($feature.Value2019,0,3) + "," + Mid($feature.Value2019,3,3),
"DEFAULT")
```

8 Click Apply and note the results.

There are still some values not formatting correctly, so you will need to add the cases for 7, 8, and 9 characters. The formatting will be the same except that it will add an additional comma.

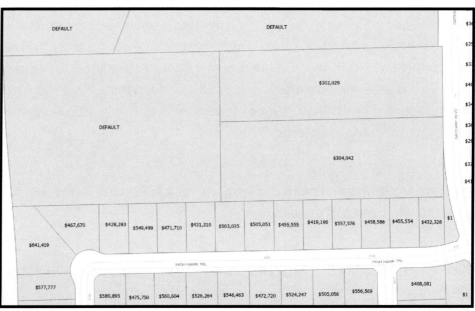

9 Copy/Paste one of the existing lines and modify to handle 7, 8, and 9 characters.

Expression
```
When(Count(Text($feature.Value2019)) <= 3,"$" + $feature.Value2019,
Count(Text($feature.Value2019)) == 4,"$" + Mid($feature.Value2019,0,1) + "," + Mid($feature.Value2019,1,3),
Count(Text($feature.Value2019)) == 5,"$" + Mid($feature.Value2019,0,2) + "," + Mid($feature.Value2019,2,3),
Count(Text($feature.Value2019)) == 6,"$" + Mid($feature.Value2019,0,3) + "," + Mid($feature.Value2019,3,3),
Count(Text($feature.Value2019)) == 7,"$" + Mid($feature.Value2019,0,1) + "," + Mid($feature.Value2019,1,3) + "," + Mid($feature.Value2019,4,3),
Count(Text($feature.Value2019)) == 8,"$" + Mid($feature.Value2019,0,2) + "," + Mid($feature.Value2019,2,3) + "," + Mid($feature.Value2019,5,3),
Count(Text($feature.Value2019)) == 9,"$" + Mid($feature.Value2019,0,3) + "," + Mid($feature.Value2019,3,3) + "," + Mid($feature.Value2019,6,3),
"DEFAULT")
```

10 Click Apply and you will see that some of the values in the million dollar range are now formatted correctly. Pan around to check the values in other areas of the map.

11 Lastly, change the default line to handle 10 characters and add three commas. Note that no condition is required for the default value.

Expression
```
When(Count(Text($feature.Value2019)) <= 3,"$" + $feature.Value2019,
Count(Text($feature.Value2019)) == 4,"$" + Mid($feature.Value2019,0,1) + "," + Mid($feature.Value2019,1,3),
Count(Text($feature.Value2019)) == 5,"$" + Mid($feature.Value2019,0,2) + "," + Mid($feature.Value2019,1,3),
Count(Text($feature.Value2019)) == 6,"$" + Mid($feature.Value2019,0,3) + "," + Mid($feature.Value2019,1,3),
Count(Text($feature.Value2019)) == 7,"$" + Mid($feature.Value2019,0,1) + "," + Mid($feature.Value2019,1,3) + "," + Mid($feature.Value2019,4,3),
Count(Text($feature.Value2019)) == 8,"$" + Mid($feature.Value2019,0,2) + "," + Mid($feature.Value2019,1,3) + "," + Mid($feature.Value2019,4,3),
Count(Text($feature.Value2019)) == 9,"$" + Mid($feature.Value2019,0,3) + "," + Mid($feature.Value2019,1,3) + "," + Mid($feature.Value2019,4,3),
"$" + Mid($feature.Value2019,0,1) + "," + Mid($feature.Value2019,1,3) + "," + Mid($feature.Value2019,4,3) + "," + Mid($feature.Value2019,7,3))
```

12 Click Apply and close the Label Class Pane. Pan around the map and see if all the values are formatting correctly. When you are satisfied, save the project. If you are continuing, keep the project open.

That was pretty complex and took a lot of careful coding to make sure all of the action was happening correctly. The end product, however, is worth the effort.

Rafael's Question—That was a lot of tight code, but it's very specifically designed for one particular field name. Is there a way I can generalize that and use it in other expressions?

Yes—how about making a user-defined function such that you feed it a number and it returns a text formatting string with commas? Then you can save this function in a text file and copy/paste it into every expression as needed. It would work like any regular Arcade function, but you get to design what it does.

Note: you will find that the expression creation panes in ArcGIS Pro include a way to save the expression to a new file. This makes them easy to document, store, and share. However, the expression panes in ArcGIS Online do not include a Save button. You can save them in a Notepad generic .TXT file. But be careful storing the files in MS Word. It has a tendency to reformat the special characters in the text such that Arcade will not recognize them.

Creating a user-defined function

User-defined functions are formatted like this:

First you put the keyword function, then the name of the function, then in parentheses you add a variable name for each input, and finally a start and stop curvy bracket. All the code you include between the curvy brackets will be executed on the input values.

For instance, if you had two values and wanted a function to convert them to a percentage, you would have your function accept the two inputs, do the math (with rounding and everything) and return a value showing percentage.

// Note that the name of the function is makepercent

function makepercent(X,Y){

   *Round(X / Y * 100,2) + "%"*

}

To use the function you would send it the two numeric values:

// Note the use of the function name makepercent()

makepercent(XVal,YVal)

... and get back ...

79.34%

It would be simple to paste this function into any expression as needed. You can modify the label expression you wrote for the property values and make it more generic. If you take the dollar signs out of the expression and replace **$feature.Value2019** with a generic variable **InValue** it can accept any value. Check the provided text file **ArcadeSampleExpressions.txt** in the projects folder of the provided material for guidance on how to make these modifications. Rafael may have typed it in there.

This new expression will use the same **When()** function but make it generic enough to use any time you want to add commas to a long number. For this exercise you can add the dollar signs back in with the return string.

1 **Open the *ArcadeSampleExpressions.txt* file from the provided projects folder. Find the commented section labeled *Exercise 8 – Sample Function*. Note that changes that were made to make it more generic.**

2 **Open the label expression builder pane for the Property Values layer. Use /* ... */ to comment out the existing expression.**

3 **Copy the function sample from the text file and paste it into the expression pane.**

Expression

```
function addcommas(InValue){
When(Count(Text(InValue)) <= 3,InValue,
Count(Text(InValue)) == 4,Mid(InValue,0,1) + "," + Mid(InValue,1,3),
Count(Text(InValue)) == 5,Mid(InValue,0,2) + "," + Mid(InValue,2,3),
Count(Text(InValue)) == 6,Mid(InValue,0,3) + "," + Mid(InValue,3,3),
Count(Text(InValue)) == 7,Mid(InValue,0,1) + "," + Mid(InValue,1,3) + "," + Mid(InValue,4,3),
Count(Text(InValue)) == 8,Mid(InValue,0,2) + "," + Mid(InValue,2,3) + "," + Mid(InValue,5,3),
Count(Text(InValue)) == 9,Mid(InValue,0,3) + "," + Mid(InValue,3,3) + "," + Mid(InValue,6,3),
Mid(InValue,0,1) + "," + Mid(InValue,1,3) + "," + Mid(InValue,4,3) + "," + Mid(InValue,7,3))
}
```

To call the function and format the value, you will use the **addcommas()** user-define function and give it the $feature.Value2019 variable. The result will be the formatted number, and you will have to add the dollar sign.

4 **Add a return statement that will use the addcommas() function to format the value (with the dollar sign added).**

```
Return "$" + addcommas($feature.Value2019)
```

5 **Validate and click Apply. If you did it correctly, you should see no difference in the formatted label! Close the Label Class pane.**

Save this **addcommas()** function – you can use it in any Arcade expression you ever write to reformat numbers to have commas. Just make sure you have the expression do all the necessary math FIRST and only format the results. It's also set for whole numbers. If you were to format a number that was rounded to two places past the decimal, the number of characters would change by 3 (a decimal and two numbers). You would then have to correct the code accordingly. You could also search for the decimal place and use that in deciding how to format the number.

Maybe you need to use periods and plus signs like they do in Europe …   2.344.345+02 . Can you write the necessary expression for that format?

> Rafael's Question—I keep seeing sample code on the Esri site that shows the use of an If / Else statement. Should I be using that?

Well Rafael, I gotta confess. There is a way to use an older format If / Else statement (note that this isn't Iif) and you can string together many conditions … but honestly you will find it easier to do the same thing with the **When()** function and I wanted to keep the book strictly Arcade where possible. The older If/Else statement is documented in the Arcade Reference if you want to see examples of how this is used.

More logic statements

There's another logic function that can be very helpful when you are dealing with coded values. Sometimes you will have a code field with an abbreviated value that represents a longer description. For instance, your zoning data may have a field called ZoneCode with values such as R1, F1, and VAC. Those codes are abbreviations representing Residential, Commercial, and Vacant zoning categories. Image having to write the When statement to decipher 23 zoning codes and write out their true description. That could be difficult.

Using the logic function **Decode()**, however, can make this job a snap. **Decode()** , much like **When(),** allows you to enter a code-value pair and will translate the codes into the included values. It can even have a default value at the end of the expression. For example, the zoning scenario describe above would be handled with this **Decode()** expression (note the inclusion of a default):

Decode($feature.ZoneCode,"R1","Residential","F1","Commercial","Vac","Vacant","Unknown")

This can have as many code-value pairs as you want.

The property data that you worked with to reformat the labels showing value also has a code for its platting status. The planning staff liked that, but now they want you to display the plat status in a pop-up along with the legal description. The fields PlatStatus, Prop-Des-1, and Prop-Des-2 are what you will need to display.

The codes for PlatStatus are:

1 = "has been platted"

2 = "has Not been platted"

3 = "has a plat pending"

4 = "has a conveyance plat only"

It would be nice to have this appear as an informative sentence:

*The property located at **Prop-Des-1, Prop-Des-2** has **Decode()***

Can you picture what the **Decode()** expression will look like? You can also add a default at the end for the null values.

1 **Continue with Exercise 8 – reopen if you closed it earlier.**

2 **Right click the Property Values layer and select Configure Pop-ups.**

3 **At the bottom of the Configure Pop-ups Pane click Expressions.**

4 **Click New and build the expression – use your own notes first, then compare to the image below. When completed and verified, click OK.**

5 Next click the Back button, then click the Edit (pencil) for the Fields list. Uncheck all the fields except your new expression at the very bottom.

For clarity, each step is on a new line. Also note the inclusion of the **Proper()** function to format the values in the property description fields.

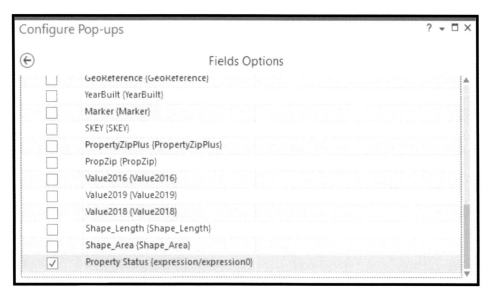

6 Click the Back button, then close the Configure Pop-ups pane.

7 Click several properties in the map to test – pan to new areas to find unplatted or plat pending values.

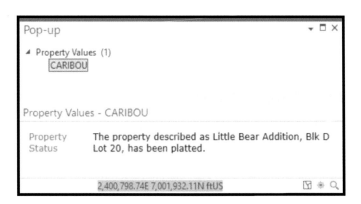

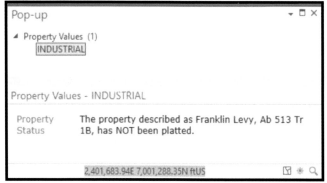

8 Save and close the project.

You can see that any fields you have that use codes or even coded value domains can be easily re-interpreted into understandable language with the **Decode()** function. You may have also discovered that you're getting pretty good at building Arcade expressions!

Chapter 6 - Working With Dates

Setting up and formatting dates in your expressions

Dates are one of the most difficult data types to work with unless you know the insider's tricks to handling them. They are a very complex data type in that a single element can hold the value for month, date, year, day of week, hour, minutes, and seconds. Extracting that data and showing in the correct format is the real trick, but totally under your control.

In Arcade, there are several functions to help you extract the information you need, and format it appropriately. There are also functions to calculate the difference between two dates, add or subtract from a date, and to even create a variable with the current date.

In this scenario, you have some iceberg data that was collected around Antarctica. The data includes the location, the first and last date that the iceberg was observed, and the first and last measured sizes (no units were provided with the data, so we'll just make them cubic meters). For an effective display, it would be nice to show the icebergs as graduated symbols indicating the change in size, and label them with the number of months they were observed. Then in the popup have a more descriptive sentence like:

*Iceberg **ID NUMBER** was first observed on **Monday, April 3, 2000,** and has **XXX** sightings recorded. It was last observed on **Monday, Sept 15, 2010,** which was **XX** years ago and showed a change in size of **XXX** cubic meters.*

Note: Items bolded in the sentence will be derived from the data.

The trick, as you may well guess, is to extract the correct information from the date field.

Exercise 9—Writing date expressions

1 **Start ArcGIS Pro and open Exercise 9. You will see a map of Antarctica showing iceberg sightings. If you wish, open the attribute table and see what the fields and data look like.**

Start with the symbology. You will need to add an expression that subtracts the value in the field Min_size from the value in the field Max_size.

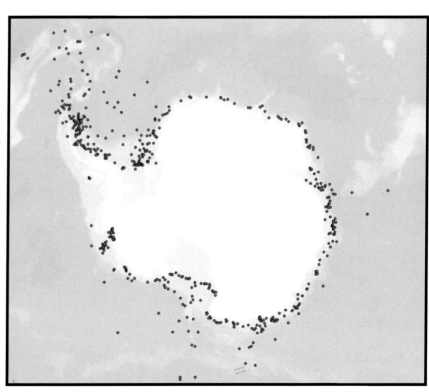

2 Open the Symbology pane, set the classification to Graduated Symbols, then click the Set an Expression button. Create the expression to subtract the two values mentioned.

Expression

`$feature.MAX_size-$feature.MIN_size`

3 Accept the defaults and close the Symbology pane.

Next you need to put the labels on the symbols showing the number of months they were observed. This will be derived by finding the difference in time between the date field MIN_Date and MAX_Date, then formatting that as Months. Research the **DateDiff()** function in the Arcade Function Reference. You will provide the function with the newest date, then the oldest date, then the format units for the output.

4 Highlight the Iceberg Tracking layer and move to the Labeling tab. Click the expression builder to open the Label Class pane.

5 Build the expression shown (verify that the correct date fields are being used in the correct order). You can also round the number to a whole integer, then zoom in to check your progress.

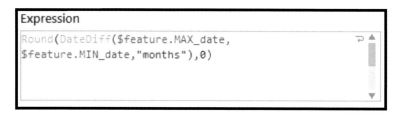

Expression

`Round(DateDiff($feature.MAX_date,`
`$feature.MIN_date,"months"),0)`

Next you will build the sentence in the pop-up. For clarity, it will be built here using variables for each of the values. It will also be easier to build and check as you go rather than try to get the entire sentence built before checking. You can try to make it into a single line expression later if you wish.

The first value is easy – it's just the iceberg's recorded ID. The second value will be the day of week. You can see from the reference page that the function **Weekday()** will return the day of week, but as an integer code from 0 to 6. You will then need to substitute an actual word in place of the number. Can you think of how to do that?

6 Right click the IceBerg layer and open the Configure Pop-ups pane. Click the Fields1 edit icon and uncheck Display, which turns all the field displays off.

7 Create a new expression called 'Iceberg Report:'.

8 Start with the first part of the sentence, adding the iceberg_ID field.

Expression

`"Iceberg " + Upper($feature.iceberg_id) + " was first observed on "`

9 Add a new variable at the top of the expression called FirstDay to hold the value of the first day of week value. The add the Weekday function and format to show the text description for the day.

```
Expression
var FirstDay = Decode(Weekday
($feature.MIN_date),0,"Sunday",1,"Monday",2,"Tuesday",3,"Wednesday",4,"Thursday",5,"Friday","Saturday")

"Iceberg " + Upper($feature.iceberg_id) + " was first observed on " + FirstDay
```

Next build three new variables to get the name of the month, the day, and the year and add them to the expression. This will use the **Month()**, **Day()**, **and Year()** functions. Look them up in the reference page to get their exact syntax.

10 **Add in the three variables called FirstMonth, FirstDate, and FirstYear and write their correct code. Then add them to the sentence.**

```
Expression
var FirstDay = Decode(Weekday
($feature.MIN_date),0,"Sunday",1,"Monday",2,"Tuesday",3,"Wednesday",4,"Thursday",5,
"Friday","Saturday")

var FirstMonth = Decode(Month
($feature.MIN_date),0,"January",1,"February",2,"March",3,"April",4,"May",5,"June",6
,"July",7,"August",8,"September",9,"October",10,"November","December")

var FirstDate = Day($feature.MIN_date)
var FirstYear = Year($feature.MIN_date)

"Iceberg " + Upper($feature.iceberg_id) + " was first observed on " + FirstDay + ",
" + FirstMonth + " " + FirstDate + ", " + FirstYear
```

On your own

You should be able to add the value for the number of sightings recorded and the date of the last observation (follow the same formatting guidelines using the fields Frequency and MAX_Date). Add those variables and put them in the sentence.

Test the pop-up and see if your sentence is looking correct.

```
Expression
var LastDay = Decode(Weekday
($feature.MAX_date),0,"Sunday",1,"Monday",2,"Tuesday",3,"Wednesday",4,"Thursday",5,
"Friday","Saturday")

var LastMonth = Decode(Month
($feature.MAX_date),0,"January",1,"February",2,"March",3,"April",4,"May",5,"June",6
,"July",7,"August",8,"September",9,"October",10,"November","December")

var LastDate = Day($feature.MAX_date)
var LastYear = Year($feature.MAX_date)

"Iceberg " + Upper($feature.iceberg_id) + " was first observed on " + FirstDay + ",
" + FirstMonth + " " + FirstDate + ", " + FirstYear + ", and has " +
$feature.FREQUENCY + " sightings recorded. It was last observed on " + LastDay + ",
" + LastMonth + " " + LastDate + ", " + LastYear + ", which was "
```

The final tricky part is to get the difference from today's date and time to the last recorded date, and show that value in years. Check the Arcade Function Reference and you will see several ways to capture today's date. The **Timestamp()** function returns today's date and time in UTC time. If you use this one, either be prepared to have all times in UTC or use the **ToLocal()** function with it. There's also a **Now()** function that returns date and time in the local time zone (whatever your machine is set for). And finally the **Today()** function will return date but with the time truncated. In this instance all the date collections are in UTC so you can continue with that.

Now that you know how to get today's date and time, you can use the **DateDiff()** function again to get the elapsed time and format it as years. Go ahead and round the number to 1 decimal place.

11 Add a variable TimePassed and calculate the elapsed time in years. Then add a variable called SizeChange. Complete the sentence and add the change in size to the sentence where appropriate.

12 Verify and apply the expression, then close the Pop-Ups pane.

```
Expression

var TimePassed = Round(DateDiff(Timestamp(),$feature.MAX_date,'years'),1)
var SizeChanged = $feature.MAX_size - $feature.MIN_size

"Iceberg " + Upper($feature.iceberg_id) + " was first observed on " + FirstDay + ",
" + FirstMonth + " " + FirstDate + ", " + FirstYear + ", and has " +
$feature.FREQUENCY + " sightings recorded. It was last observed on " + LastDay + ",
" + LastMonth + " " + LastDate + ", " + LastYear + ", which was " + TimePassed + "
years ago and showed a change in size of " + SizeChanged + " cubic meters."

    ✓  Expression is valid
```

13 Select an iceberg and note the pop-up.

14 If you are not continuing, save and close Exercise 9.

Note: There are several functions to pull the date and time in UTC versus local time, and functions to convert from local to UTC. Make sure you watch time zones carefully to avoid having hours of time discrepancies in your analysis.

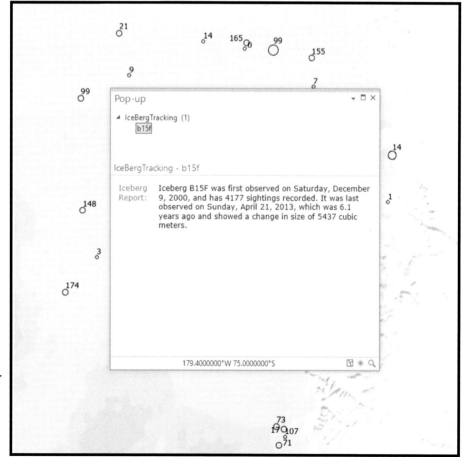

Pop-up   ▾ ☐ ✕

◢ IceBergTracking (1)
   b15f

IceBergTracking - b15f

Iceberg   Iceberg B15F was first observed on Saturday, December
Report: 9, 2000, and has 4177 sightings recorded. It was last
           observed on Sunday, April 21, 2013, which was 6.1
           years ago and showed a change in size of 5437 cubic
           meters.

179.4000000°W 75.0000000°S

Using the Date() function

There was a lot of typing in that one, and you had to be very particular to get every parenthesis and plus sign in the right place. But the result is very nice!

And while this exercise didn't calculate hours and minutes, you can see that the **Hour()** and **Minute()** functions work exactly the same way as the **Day()** and **Month()** functions.

There's an addition function called **Date()** that can be used to reformat data from other sources into true date fields. For example, if you received data that came from an Excel spreadsheet, the date fields may have the right syntax but ArcGIS Pro won't treat it like a true date field. This would prevent you from using any of the date formatting fields that you just used in the first part of this exercise. By reformatting with the **Date()** function you can extract all the normal date type information from the field.

In this second half of Exercise 9, you are given some data from the Fire Department that was extracted from their call dispatching system. When that system was written, the programmers thought it would be very handy to place all of the date and time information into separate fields rather than deal with a complex date field. As a result the dispatch time and arrival times are each spread across six different fields. The chief wants you to make a map showing the elapsed response time from dispatch to arrival, but dealing with 12 fields and trying to figure out that calculation is next to impossible to do. Instead you will use the **Date()** function to reformat the sets of fields, then it will be a snap to find the elapsed time with the **DateDiff()** function.

1 **Re-open Exercise 9, if you had closed it before, and move to the Fire Department map.**

2 **Examine the table for the Calls For Service layer and note the last 12 fields and the data they contain.**

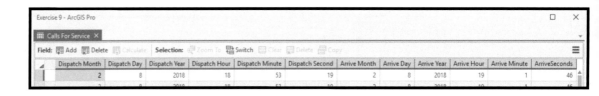

They are all short integers, so they will be a perfect fit with the codes used in the Arcade date field – with one exception. The index for months in Arcade are 0 to 11 and in this data they are 1 to 12. Just remember to subtract 1 from the number when converting to the date field. Research the **Date()** function in the function reference and note the order in which the data must be included. The first entry will be the year field, which will then inform the function that you are formatting a date from multiple fields.

Your goal is to symbolize the data with graduated symbols based on the response times. You will make two variables in the expression to convert the fields into two date fields, then do the final calculation and return a value for the symbol generator.

3 Open the Symbology pane and set to Graduated Symbols. Then open the expression pane and change the title to Response Time.

4 Start with the variable for the dispatch time, and call it DispTime. Then add the six fields necessary to make the date – make sure to get them in the proper order and to subtract 1 from the month code.

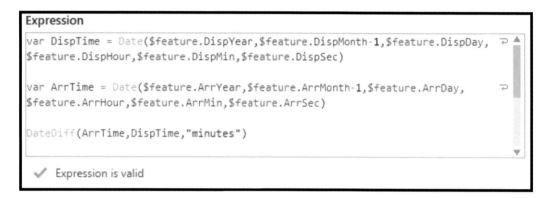

```
Expression
var DispTime = Date($feature.DispYear,$feature.DispMonth-1,$feature.DispDay,
$feature.DispHour,$feature.DispMin$feature.DispSec)
```

5 Next add the variable for ArrivTime and format the fields with the Date() function.

6 Finally, add the DateDiff() function using the two variables and set the output units to minutes.

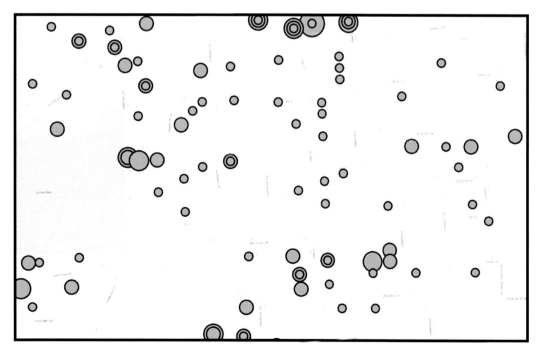

```
Expression
var DispTime = Date($feature.DispYear,$feature.DispMonth-1,$feature.DispDay,
$feature.DispHour,$feature.DispMin,$feature.DispSec)

var ArrTime = Date($feature.ArrYear,$feature.ArrMonth-1,$feature.ArrDay,
$feature.ArrHour,$feature.ArrMin,$feature.ArrSec)

DateDiff(ArrTime,DispTime,"minutes")
```
✓ Expression is valid

7 Reset the color and/or adjust the size if you like. After inspecting the results you can save and close Exercise 9.

As you can see, handling date fields isn't terribly hard but there are some specific tricks you need to understand. Once you know these you won't be afraid to use dates to their fullest – even if some knucklehead puts all the date information in 12 separate fields!

Chapter 7—Writing Geometry Functions

Arcade has specific code to handle geometry features directly

Geometry functions with Arcade work with ... you guessed it ... the points, lines, and polygons within your layers and can access information about their field values and their positions. For instance, you can find the area of a polygon or the length of a line; you can see if items intersect, overlap, or have nothing in common; and you can split features and calculate new areas. Many of the things that you would do with regular analysis tools you can do with Arcade, and the results can either be used on-the-fly for labels, pop-ups, or visualization but can also be calculated and stored in an attribute in the table.

This first scenario is very simple but when you stop and think about what it's doing you will realize why this is important. The property values layer that you have been working with has a field called Acreage. There's several ways to calculate the value for this, but for this example you will do it with Arcade.

The key is in using the $feature variable to reference the layer along with the **Area()** function. You only need to identify the output units in the expression. A quick look at the Arcade Function Reference will show what the key words are for the different units, as well as the syntax for the function.

At the top of the Arcade Geometry Functions page is a very important message. This is a warning that the results from the geometry functions are dependent on the viewing scale and resolution of the features. Bottom line – the results can change when you zoom and pan your map. They won't be large, dramatic changes but rather small changes measured several places past the decimal. However, don't rely on these to be the most accurate, consistent, predicable, and scientific result! If you need that kind of precision, then you are going to have to resort to adding fields and using the geoprocessing tools rather than on-the-fly Arcade expressions.

You should also know that complex geometry functions use a lot of compute power. If you are wanting to use these with your AGOL apps, be prepared for a bit of a wait while they execute.

You've been warned!! You also get warned on every function reference. Now that you know what you're getting in to ...

Exercise 10—Working with the Area() function

You will start with a simple geometry function, then explore some of the more complex functions and their uses in the following exercises.

1 **Open Exercise 10. The Property Data maps contains the familiar parcel layout.**

2 **Open the attribute table and find the Acreage field. Right click the field name and select Calculate Field.**

3 **Change the Expression Type to Arcade.**

From researching the syntax, you will know that the expression you want to write is:

Area($feature,"acres")

4 In the code area, type in the Arcade Function as shown in the figure at the right. When your code matches what is show, validate and click Run.

It's not a big deal with this little expression, but as these get more complex you will want to use the Export button to save a copy for future use.

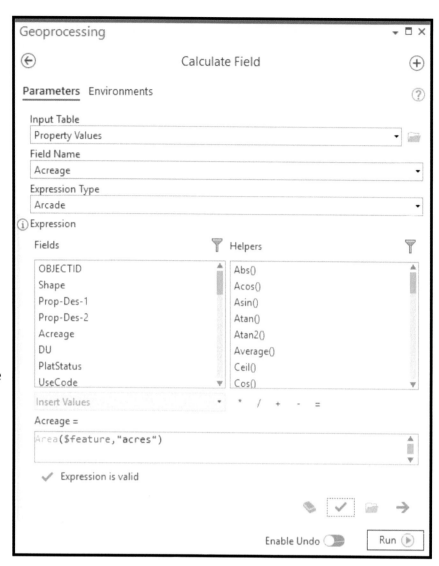

5 Check the attribute table to verify that the calculation was done. When finished, close the attribute table, then save and close the project.

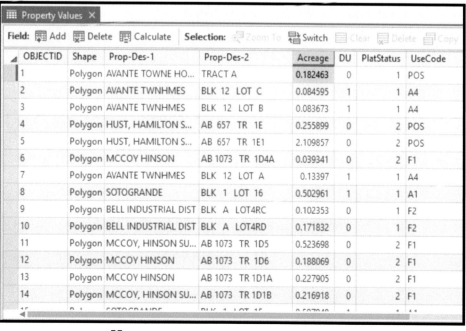

That one was pretty easy, but you see how the Arcade geometry functions are used.

The function used was able to access the internal structure of the geometry and determine the area, then convert that to your chosen units. There are other measurement functions such as finding the centroid or length.

Some of the other functions go further than that and allow you to access the geometry of multiple layers at the same time in order to have your expression do some overlay analysis. These include clipping or intersecting, buffering, and even topology functions like finding inside/outside conditions or adjacency conditions.

Writing geometry analysis expressions in ArcGIS Online

The next scenario will use your ArcGIS Online account. The Federal Communications Commission oversees all antennas in the United States and wants to make sure that they are kept in good order. As each license is renewed an inspection is done before re-certifying the antenna. As a cost saving measure, they are considering paying local counties $100 per antenna to do this. This is an optional program for counties and they want to be able to provide a count of antennas for each county so that the local administrators can decide if they would like to participate. The county boundary data is pretty static, but the number of antennas is always changing so there needs to be a way for the county official to look this up and get a very current and accurate count. You will make a web map that has the county boundaries and the antenna registry, then build an Arcade expression to calculate this on the fly.

Note: Currently the overlay tools for this type of process only work in a limited number of profiles, so you will need to configure this in the pop-ups rather than as a visible label. Also, this whole payment scheme is a fantasy scenario invented by the author.

Exercise 11—Overlay analysis in AGOL

For this process you will use the **Extent()** function, the **Contains()** function and the **Count()** function. Research these in the Arcade Function Reference and get an idea of the syntax. You will also work with the global **$map** variable which will allow you to access all the feature layers in the current map.

1 Open ArcGIS Online and create a new map.

2 Click Add > Browse Living Atlas Layers and search for the layers USA Counties (Generalized) and Antenna Structure Registrate, adding each to the map as they are found.

3 Once these are added, zoom in to any area you like. Create labels to show the county names and set the transparency of the counties layer to about 50%. You may also want to set a maximum visible scale on the antennas.

4 Under the USA Counties layer, click the options button and select Configure Pop-ups.

5 Scroll down to the Attribute Expression area and click Add Expression.

The pane that opens allows you to write code in the Expression area and access variables, functions, and constants at the right. There's also a Test button so that you can see if your expression is working.

You will be using the **Contains()** function but first you need to establish the area that you will use for the function. This is done by making a variable which will hold the current extent, using the **Extent()** function.

6 At the top click the Edit button and change the name to County Antennas, then click Save.

7 In the Expression box, type the code shown to make a variable and store the feature layer's extent .

The next part will make a pretty long line of code, and it will scroll off your screen. Some trickery is used here to display the entire code.

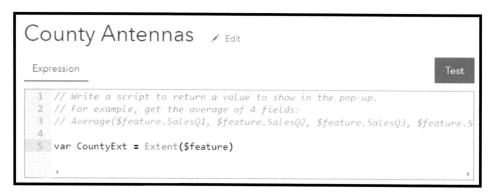

You will first start the creation of a variable called AntCount. After that you will configure the **Contains()** function, then encase it in the **Count()** function. If you like, you can use the Functions tab to find and add the appropriate functions, but it will probably be easier just to type them in.

8 Press Enter to start a new line. Type in *var AntCount = .*

9 Then type in *Count(.* Note that the closing parentheses is automatically added.

10 Next type *Contains(.*

This will set up the structure for the functions, and notice that there is a red X to the left of the line indicating that they aren't properly configured (yet).

11 Type in the new variable name of CountyExt followed by a comma.

12 Make sure the Globals tab is selected and click the > to the right of $maps to expand the choice of layers in the map.

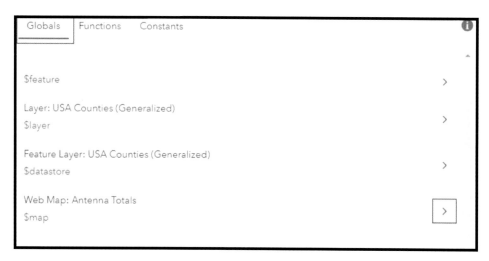

13 Under the heading Layer: Antenna Structure Registrate click the item FeatureSetByID(...)

This has added the last part of the expression line.

```
1  // Write a script to return a value to show in the pop-up.
2  // For example, get the average of 4 fields:
3  // Average($feature.SalesQ1, $feature.SalesQ2, $feature.SalesQ3, $feature.SalesQ4)
4
5  var CountyExt = Extent($feature)
6  var AntCount = Count(Contains(CountyExt,FeatureSetById($map,"Antenna_Structure_Registrate_5913")))
7
```

Rafael's Question: Wait!?! What exactly did this do?

The **Extent()** function will store the extent of each feature as it is selected. Then the **Contains()** function will look at the antenna features and see if they are within this extent. If so they get a True value and if not they get a False value. A feature set of the True values is created. Finally, the **Count()** function will count the number of features in the feature set. That's how many antennas are in the county! Each time you select a county the pop-up will run this expression and provide the correct count.

Finally you will format a Return statement to provide a nice sentence rather than just a bare number. It will also be helpful to round it to a whole number (Arcade has a tendency to show two decimal places unless told otherwise).

14 Add a Return statement with an appropriate sentence. It should include the Round() function and the AntCount variable. In this example, the name of the county was also included.

```
1  // Write a script to return a value to show in the pop-up.
2  // For example, get the average of 4 fields:
3  // Average($feature.SalesQ1, $feature.SalesQ2, $feature.SalesQ3, $feature.SalesQ4)
4
5  var CountyExt = Extent($feature)
6  var AntCount = Count(Contains(CountyExt,FeatureSetById($map,"Antenna_Structure_Registrate_5913")))
7  Return $feature.NAME + " County has " + Round(AntCount,0) + " antennas in it."
```

15 Click Test to see if your code is working, and repair as necessary. When it tests without errors, click OK.

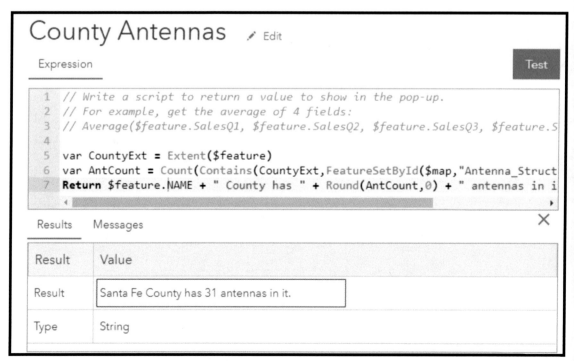

County Antennas ✎ Edit

Expression   Test

```
1  // Write a script to return a value to show in the pop-up.
2  // For example, get the average of 4 fields:
3  // Average($feature.SalesQ1, $feature.SalesQ2, $feature.SalesQ3, $feature.S
4
5  var CountyExt = Extent($feature)
6  var AntCount = Count(Contains(CountyExt,FeatureSetById($map,"Antenna_Struct
7  Return $feature.NAME + " County has " + Round(AntCount,0) + " antennas in i
```

Results   Messages   ✕

Result	Value
Result	Santa Fe County has 31 antennas in it.
Type	String

16 Back in the Configure Pop-Up pane, click Configure Attributes and turn off all the attributes except Population and County Antennas. Click OK.

17 Pan around the map and click on several counties to see their antenna totals.

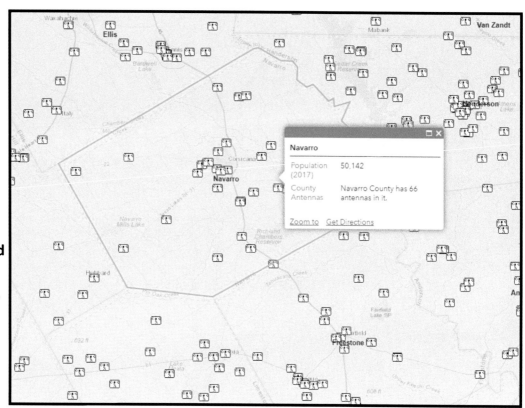

Navarro

Population (2017)   50,142

County Antennas   Navarro County has 66 antennas in it.

Zoom to   Get Directions

18 When you are satisfied with the results, save your map. If you are continuing, keep ArcGIS Online open.

You can imagine the possibilities of using those techniques with other geometry functions. You could buffer and intersect features, or calculate how much area is not covered by paving, or total up the area of forests clipped by harvest area ... all on the fly and without having to add fields to the attribute table (which you may not be able to do anyway).

It's interesting to note that the **Contains()** function created a feature set. This feature set could be used for other things, like making an array or using it to do averages or minimums/maximums.

More Geometry Functions

This next scenario will work with flood plain data and more of the geometry functions. The City Engineer has asked you to prepare a total of the number of houses that fall within the flood plain. You are provided the flood plain polygons and the building footprint polygons, and the flood plain layer has a field called House Count into which you can place the totals.

You saw earlier the profiles in which Arcade is relevant, and one of those is the Field Calculate profile. That's where this action will take place, but with any good programming you will first need to figure out how the process will work before trying to write the code.

First you need to determine how you will reference the two layers for this expression. Since you will be using the field calculator in the Flood Zones layer, that layer will be referenced as $feature. In other words, each feature in the layer will be involved individually in the calculation. Then the Building Footprints layer will be referenced through the **$datastore** variable, since this global variable can reference all the other layers in the same map.

There are two choices for referencing the Building Footprints layer... FeatureSetByName or FeatureSetByID. Either one will work, but best practices says to use the ID since it is least likely to change at the whim of the cartographer.

Checking topology conditions with Arcade

Next you will use the **Overlaps()** function to build the feature set of the building outlines that overlap the selected flood zone. It will do a polygon on polygon overlay and discover how many buildings are inside the flood zone polygon. Note that even though the flood zones layer has multiple features, the command will automatically iterate through the features and perform the overlay once for each feature.

And FINALLY you will do a **Count()** function on the results of the **Overlaps()** function to see how many houses were identified as overlapping the flood zone. And of course the Return function will send the result back to the field.

Exercise 12—Geometry layer overlap condition

This exercise will also be done in ArcGIS Online – mainly because the Arcade expression building interface is so nice and also because it is much more visual and easier to understand. You will start by opening an exercise and sharing it as a web map to your AGOL account.

1 **Open Exercise 12 in ArcGIS Pro and make sure you are logged in to your AGOL account (if necessary).**

2 **In the Share tab, look in the Share As section and click Web map.**

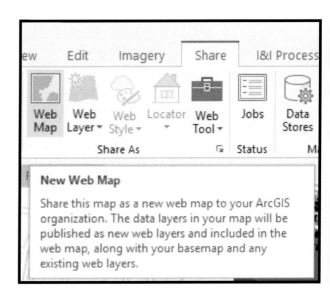

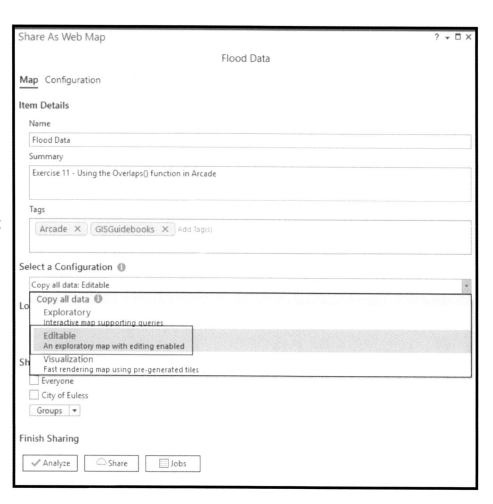

3 **Provide a Name, Summary, and Tags. Then click the Select a Configuration box and select Editable. Set the folders and sharing however you like and click Share.**

4 **Close ArcGIS Pro and move to your AGOL account. Find the new Flood Data web map and open it in Map Viewer.**

5 **Click the Flood Zones layer and then click Show Table.**

The table will open at the bottom of the screen.

6 Click on the field name House Count and select Calculate. (Note this is a left click)

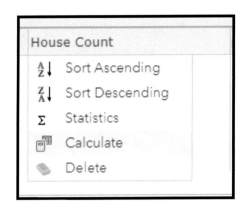

7 Then choose Arcade as the language of choice.

Now comes the code. Start with the **Overlaps()** function and add the name of the buildings layer from the data store, and the current layer (which is the flood zones).

8 Type in *Overlaps(* , then click the More arrow to the right of $datastore. Then under Layer: Building Footprints, click on FeatureSetById(…) .

The entire string necessary to reference this layer in the datastore is added in one click. Note that it includes a comments section to remind you of which layer this is referencing. In the next images this will be removed for clarity but in real practice you should leave that in.

9 After the first close parentheses type a comma. Then click the Back button on the Globals area, and click on $feature.

The last step is to enclose the **Overlaps()** function in the **Count()** function and add the Return keyword.

10 At the start of the expression type the *Return* keyword followed by *Count(* . Finally, add a close parentheses at the end of the expression

There is no SAVE button in the expression generator, so you might want to highlight your entire expression and copy/paste it into a document somewhere to save it.

If there are any errors in your expression, there are two ways to see them. First there will be a red X in the left margin next to the line with the error. Then when you click the Test button you will get any error messages in a text dialog at the bottom of the Expression area. If there are no errors, it will return a sample value showing what the expected outcome will be.

11 **Click Test to see if you have any errors. Fix any, then press OK. Be patient, it takes a while to kick off, then take a while to run.**

12 **When it finishes, you should see house counts for each zone code type.**

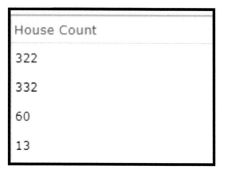

House Count
322
332
60
13

Let's explain to Rafael what happened before he asks. The expression took the first flood zone area, matched it against the building footprints and built a feature set of the ones that overlapped. Then it counted them and wrote the results to the field House Count. Then it took the second flood zone area and repeated the action – writing the results to the House Count field for the second feature. This repeated for all of the features in the Flood Zones layer. In our case, four but it could be any number.

The things to watch for are that you keep your code concise to minimize the number of queries it has to do, and you probably wouldn't want to run this on a huge dataset. It would take quite a while to complete!

On your own

Add a field to the Flood Zones layer and calculate the area of each flood zone in square miles. This will be very similar but will use the **Area()** function for each zone. Check the Arcade Reference for the units key words. Hint: You won't need the **Count()** or **Overlaps()** functions.

13 Save your web map, but keep it open if you are continuing.

Square Miles
1.70
0.14
0.58
0.07

Building Array() and Dictionary() items

In this same web map, there another thing they are asking for. The Property Values layer has a land use code, and they would like to be able to click a property and see that information. But instead of seeing the use code such as "B1" or "I2" they want to see a more descriptive code such as "Multi-Family Residential" or "Light Industrial". This will be done in the Popup profile and will use a lookup dictionary to display a translated land use code. The land use codes and their translated descriptions are shown in this chart:

Use Code	Translation
A1	Single Family Detached
A2	Single Family - Duplex
A3	Single Family - Triplex
A4	Single Family - Quadruplex
A5	Single Family - Limited
AFAC	Airport Facilities
APR	Airport
B1	Multi-Family Residential Low Density
B2	Multi-Family Residential Medium Density
B3	Multi-Family Residential High Density
B4	Multi-Family Residential Urban Lofts
CITY	City Property
CITYV	Vacant City Property
CITYW	Water Utility Property
CRH	Church
ESMT	Easement
F1	Commercial
F2	Industrial
GOV	Government (State or Federal)
POS	Public Open Space
PRK	Park Land
PROW	Private Right-of-way
ROW	Public Right-of-way
SCH	School
UNK	Unknown
UTIL	Utility
VAC	Vacant

It might also be nice to show some summary statistics such as the area of the land they chose, the total amount of that type of zoning in the city, and what percent this property represents.

Working in the Arcade Playground

All of these things can be done in the web map you created for Exercise 12. If you did not complete that exercise, open the Exercise 12 project and use it to create a web map (see steps 1 through 4 for how to do this).

The tools to test are the **Array()** and **Dictionary()** functions. It's important to see how these work and how you will call them in your expression. You know you're supposed to look these up in the Arcade Reference before going on.

An **Array[]** is a special type of variable that can hold multiple values. These can be text or numeric, or even both in the same array. The values are included in a set of square brackets, separated by commas. The values will be given an internal index number starting from the left with zero. So if your array has 10 values, they will be indexed from zero to nine. To call a value from an array, you give the name of the array and include the index number of the desired value in square brackets. There's a sample array with the book materials for you to experiment with.

Exercise 13—Testing code in the playground

Before you start working with the data, it might be interesting to try out some of the commands in the ArcGIS Arcade Playground. This is located on the same page as the Function Reference … just click the Playground tab.

1 **Browse to the files you downloaded for this book and n the Projects folder, find and open the Arcade Sample Expressions.txt file.**

Quick warning – open this file in Notepad. If you open it in MS Word the quotes will be changed from a standard quote to a start and end quote, which Arcade doesn't recognize.

2 **Open a web browser and go to the Arcade Function Reference. Click the Playground tab.**

3 **Copy the three lines for Sample 1 and paste them into the Playground Expression. Then click Test. Note – the image shows the array on multiple lines for clarity.**

The index value of 3 returned the fourth value – Commercial.

4 **Try changing the index value and clicking Test to see what values will be returned.**

This method will return the array value when it is specifically called, but what if you need to go through all the values in the array? In Sample 2, a FOR loop is used to run through the array and concatenate all the values into a single string. The format of the FOR loop is to have the function **for()**, and within the parentheses have an index variable to keep track of the iterations; the key word IN; and the name of the array. Following this statement are a pair of curvy brackets. The code placed between the curvy brackets will be executed for each iteration of the loop. The loop will stop when all of the values in the array have been evaluated.

5 **Copy and paste Sample 2 from the text file into the Playground Expression. Click Test to run it.**

Note that the variable Answer is declared before the FOR loop starts. Then within the loop (between the curvy brackets) it is concatenated to itself and the next value in the array, separated by a forward slash. Then the final string is returned when the loop has finished.

In this next sample, we are assuming that the expression is pulling a property value from a table, and the user is selecting which percentage calculation they would like to perform on that value. The choices are 25%, 50%, 75%, or 100%. For testing, those values are hard coded into the expression but in rea use might be selected from a menu or drop-down dialog box.

The array of percentages is created, then a loop is used to find the correct value as selected by the user, do the math, and return a properly formatted answer.

6 **Copy and paste Sample 3 from the text file into the Playground Expression. Click Test to run it. Try changing the value of User Selection to use a different percentage in the array.**

Note that the UserSelection value is used with the array to pull the correct value.

Another interesting type of array is a Dictionary. A dictionary stores **value pairs**, and when one value is called, the paired valued is returned. These are especially useful when you are pulling a code value from a table and you want to translate it into a text description --- hey, just like what you want to do with the land use codes. The values go into a dictionary the same way as an array except that you put in two values as a pair.

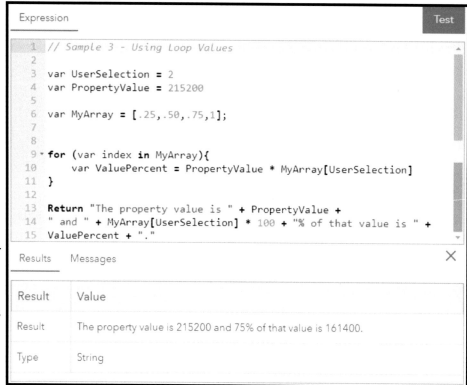

7 **Copy and paste Sample 4 from the text file into the Playground Expression. Click Test to run it. Change the dictionary value to TRDPT and see the different results.**

There is also a Sample 5 that shows another way to format a dictionary and recall a value. The values are set between curvy brackets and separated by a colon. The value can be recalled by typing the dictionary name, followed by a dot, followed by the dictionary code. Note that n' quotes are needed when recalling the values.

Try out sample 5 if you like. The functionality is the same, it just uses a different format.

This format is particularly useful for very long dictionaries, and is the format you will use for the land use codes. In fact, Example 6 in the text file is the dictionary for this exercise. Try pasting that into the Playground for testing.

```
1  //Sample 5 - Dictionary 2
2
3  var BldCodes = {
4    "BDPT":"Bus Depot",
5    "TRDPT":"Train Depot"
6  }
7
8  return BldCodes.TRDPT;
```

No. This dictionary was made by doing a Summary on the field in the layer's table. That produced a table with one row for each land use code. Then the table was exported to Excel where the quotes and translated descriptions were added. Then a new column was made between them and a colon inserted, then the same to put a comma at the end. The whole thing was then copy/pasted into Notepad and formatted as an Arcade expression. There's still work to make these, but a lot of time was saved discovering all the codes and adding the formatting marks.

Putting a dictionary to use

Now that you know how you will translate the code in the table into a description, take a look at how the rest of the pop-up will work.

Finding the land use code of the selected property is easy – it's a field in the layer's table that is referenced as $feature.UseCode. You'll want to store that in a variable for the complex calculations later – so maybe CurrCode = $feature.useCode .

You can build the dictionary called LandUseCodes shown in the text samples, and recall any of the values with the expression LandUseCodes[CurrCode], which will return the description and not the code.

They want to see the total area of the selected property – and that's just the Shape_Area field. They also want to see the total of the particular type of land use that you chose. For instance, if you click on a park, show the total area of parks in the city. This is done with the **Sum()** function. This function can sum a series of numbers, but if you give it a layer and a field in that layer, it will sum all the values from the entire layer. However, that's not what you want; you only want the total of the chosen land use. The solution is to add a **Filter()** function to the expression (research this in the Arcade reference). This allows you to add a query and select features out of the layer that meet the query. In this case, you will look for where the field UseCode equals the current code value CurrCode.

Once you have the area of the feature and the total area of that land use type, calculating the percentage is easy. It's just math.

With the inclusion of this long dictionary, this will be a very long expression so the images here will only show portions of the dialogs at a time. Each value will be calculated separately then combined at the end. Use the expression building aids in the Globals pane – don't just copy the code from the images. Learn to find the items for yourself and add them as needed.

Continuing with exercise 13 in ArcGIS Online, you will first set up the dictionary.

1 **Open the Flood Data web map in the map viewer, if necessary, and turn off the Flood Zones and Building Footprints layers.**

2 **Open the Configure Pop-up pane and add a new Attribute Expression. Change the name to Area Statistics.**

3 **Copy the dictionary declaration from the provided text file and paste it into the new expression.**

4 Next, add the variable CurrCode and have it retrieve the value from the UseCode field in the layer. Then add a variable CodeDesc to store the description retrieved from the dictionary.

Area Statistics ✏ Edit

Expression   Test

```
22   "PRK"   :    "Park Land" ,
23   "PROW"  :    "Private Right-of-way"  ,
24   "ROW"   :    "Public Right-of-way"   ,
25   "SCH"   :    "School"    ,
26   "UNK"   :    "Unknown"   ,
27   "UTIL"  :    "Utility"   ,
28   "VAC"   :    "Vacant"
29   }
30
31   var CurrCode = $feature.UseCode
32   var CodeDesc = LandUseCodes[CurrCode]
33
34
```

The area calculations will begin with retrieving the area of the selected feature.

5 **Now make a variable that will store the area of the current feature called FeatArea. Then add a variable called SumArea to store the area of all features (you'll apply the filter later).**

```
33
34   var FeatArea = $feature["Shape__Area"]
35   var SumArea = sum($layer,"Shape__Area")
36
37
```

To add a filter to the **Sum()** function, you will bracket the $layer keyword with **Filter()**, add a comma, then add an SQL expression to represent the features you want to select. In this case, find where the field Use-Code equals whatever the current selected code is. Now here's the trick – the dictionary command can't be inserted into this SQL query but an Arcade variable can. Since the value is stored in the CurrCode variable, this can be inserted into the query. To do this you preface the variable name with an 'at' sign, so your query becomes "UseCode = @CurrCode".

6 **Add the Filter() function to the SumArea variable expression.**

```
34   var FeatArea = $feature["Shape__Area"]
35   var SumArea = sum(Filter($layer,"UseCode = @CurrCode"),"Shape__Area")
36
```

7 **Now add a variable called Percent to calculate the percent of area the current feature represents. That will be the area of the feature divided by the total area, multiplied times 100.**

```
38
39   Return "The property you have selected has a land use of " + CodeDesc +
40   ". There is a total of " + Round(SumArea/43560,2) +
41   " acres of this type of land use in the city. " +
42   "The area of this property is " + Round(FeatArea/43560,2) +
43   " acres and that represents " + Round(Percent,2) +
44   "% of the total for this land use."
45
```

That's all the data needed to make a full report. See if you can format the sentence below before looking at the image. And the kicker … the values from the layer are in square feet but the pop-up should show acres. Hint, there are 43560 square feet in an acre.

8 **Add a Return expression to make this sentence (with value substitutions where appropriate):**

*The property you have selected has a land use of **CodeDesc**. There is a total of **SumArea** acres of this type of land use in the city. The area of this property is **FeatArea** acres and that represents **Percent**% of the total for this land use.*

9 **Click OK to save the expression, then set the Configure Attributes list to only display the new expression you built. Click OK to finish. You can symbolize the layer by UseCode if you like.**

10 **Pan around the map and select properties so that you can admire your handywork. Well done!**

11 Save the map, and exit ArcGIS Online.

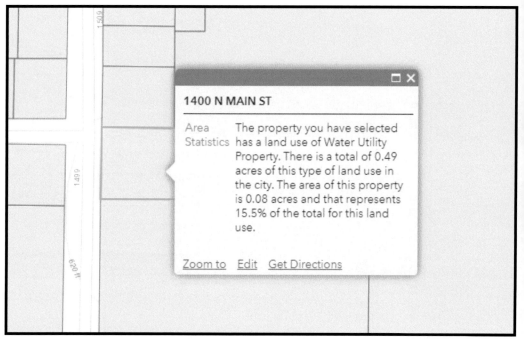

There are a LOT more cool Arcade functions, and it's impossible to write exercises that highlight them all and include them in this book. But the Rafael's Challenge at the end will provide you with some more ideas that you can try out on your own.

For further study, watch the ArcGIS Arcade Blog posts at https://www.esri.com/arcgis-blog/overview/ and search for Arcade. The Esri staff periodically post new ideas on uses of Arcade and hopefully the basics in this book will help you to better understand their demonstrations.

Rafael's Challenge

This is the last part of the books, and if you've made it this far and gotten all the exercises completed successfully, then Congratulations! You should be able to write some pretty impressive Arcade expressions. But now the BIG CHALLENGE!!

It seems that Rafael has been doing very well in his GIS classes and now wants to show off a bit. So he challenges YOU to complete these final challenges on your own. You have already learned the techniques and tools necessary to complete them, and each has a scenario description and references the necessary data.

Can you beat Rafael at his own game?

Challenge Number 1

In Exercise 1 you showed the total appraised value for property in a pop-up. Add a value to the pop-up to show the dollar per square foot ... but only if it has a structure on it. Hint: Research the **IsNull()** function and use that to determine when the value should be displayed.

Challenge Number 2

In Exercise 3 you worked with some census demographic data. You didn't configure a pop-up for the Populated Places layer, but now they would like a pop-up that shows the place name and the estimated number of unemployed citizens. Use the 2012 population total from the place name layer and the 2016 Unemployment Rate from the Daytime Population layer (we'll mix and match a bit, but it's just an exercise).

Challenge Number 3

The antenna data used in Exercise 10 has a field called Structure height (in meters). Have the popup box show the average antenna height, as well as the single tallest antenna. Research the **Mean()** and **Max()** functions. Extra credit – have the pop-up list the 5 tallest antennas. Hint: Look at using a FOR loop to find antenna heights and save the top 5. Extra EXTRA credit – build a pop-up for the Antenna Structure Registrate layer such that when you click an antenna it will tell you the entity that owns it, and how many other antennas they own in that county.

Challenge Number 4

In Exercise 6 you built some interesting statistics, and the dataset contained many other interesting fields with values for both 2016 and 2021. Create more values showing these other types of analysis.

♦ Change in Divorce Rate

♦ Change in Group Quarters Population

♦ Change in the Number of Baby Boomers as a percentage of the total population

♦ Change in Vacant Housing Unit Count as a percentage of the total number of housing units

Challenge Number 5

The Exercise 13 data included building footprints (and you now have it as a web map). Write an expression such that when you click on a building footprint a pop-up will tell you the value of the property, the square footage of the building, the year it was built, and the flood zone. Extra credit – don't display the flood zone data unless the value is not null. Hint: research the **IsEmpty()** function.

Made in the USA
Monee, IL
25 August 2020